Arthur Berry can recall in detail his childhood and youthful experiences in the pit village of Smallthorne and the nearby Pottery town of Burslem. Indeed, the impression they made on him has set the seal on all his work.

"Burslem," he says, "was only a mile away and through my childhood the streets I grew up in seemed filled with character. It was a town of a thousand smoking chimneys. The subjects of my paintings were the entries between the houses, the old women smoking pipes at their house doors, the men smoking fag-ends at street corners, the short tailed mongrels roaming the streets. There was much poverty in this world, much illness: the air was so thick you could chew it. Reasonable people said it resembled an anteroom to hell; but to me it was paradise."

In the LITTLE GOLD-MINE he recreates the scenes and the sometimes bizarre characters he knew and in the harsh, often humorous language of the streets, tells how they strove against the odds to make their marks in their little world — and how one woman succeeded.

The Little Gold-Mine

by

Arthur Berry

**Illustrations by the author
Arthur Berry**

Cover picture by Alan Fraser

Published by
BULLFINCH PUBLICATIONS,
245 Hunts Cross Avenue,
Woolton, Liverpool L25 9ND

Produced By
THOMAS LOUGHLIN,
Mulberry House, Canning Place,
Liverpool L1 8JG.
Tel: 051-709 0818

British Library Cataloguing in Publication Data.
    A catalogue record for this book is available from the
    British Library.

ISBN 0-9511427-7-1

A note from the Author

The idea for this book came from an unusual source. I was reading in some magazine or other that the late King Ibn Saud who, when asked what had been his greatest pleasures in life, said without hesitation that he had enjoyed first perfume, then horses and then women in that order. I was somewhat surprised at this especially him putting women last. Perhaps having always had a harem filled with great beauties had taken the edge off sex for him. After all if you do anything long enough, it will turn to scrubbing. But sitting thinking about the question, I put it to myself, what had I enjoyed most in this passage through conscious existence. As usual, whenever I try to answer any of the profound questions about this life I was soon floundering in a sea of half truths. On this occasion for some reason I persisted, and after much if-ing and aah-ing I did manage to make my own little list.

Number three of my pleasures is undoubtedly an armchair. I have always been a lazy kind of man, who, fortunately, enjoys the feeling of having worked to such an extent that I always just about manage to maul myself up from a recumbent position to make the effort to do something so that my life should not be a total waste. But it is always against my deepest inclination, which is to stay snoozing in my armchair.

The next of my pleasures, number two on my list, are animals. All my life there has been a stream of love between myself and dogs and cats and almost any other animal of reasonable size. The fact that they have dark wet noses on the end of their faces and are covered in fur and have tails at the end of their bodies and scratch for fleas and are altogether simpler in their way of being alive than human beings has always had great appeal to me. In fact I think that if people were covered in fur, often dappled, and had dark wet noses, and pee'd on car wheels and lamp posts, I should perhaps love them more, but I am not sure about this. People can be such crossomical buggers at times. But with dogs and cats you always know where you are and my love for them is without qualifications.

The last and yet the first of my earthly pleasures was more difficult to decide on. It had to be fought out between two contenders. Number one was beef dripping toast, heavily sprinkled with salt. This to me was the food of the Gods. Nothing I have ever put in my mouth can equal it. No vocables or syllables I could possibly arrange can come anywhere near describing it's succulent magnificence. It is years since I tasted it but the memory still plagues my mind. What a bleak and sad day it was that I read in some newspaper that of all foods known to civilised man it was the deadliest. Oh woe was me on that black day. Nothing has ever been able to take the place of beef dripping on toast. But I must be fair as I can manage, for I have to look at my life as a whole, when attempting to answer this question fairly. After much deliberation I have come to the conclusion that from being a young boy up and down the first streets of my life, to being a rather world weary adult, chips have been such a main and pleasurable prop to my existence that I must award them the first place in my list. Having decided this I began to think of how I could pay a proper homage to this cheap and earthy food, bags of which have warmed my ribs on many a winter's night, and this book is my attempt to do it.

ILLUSTRATIONS

**The story of a little gold-mine,
how it came into being how it prospered
and how it eventually ran out of gold.**

Introduction

First I will introduce myself. My name is Enoch Salt. I was named, I am told, after a long dead uncle of mine, known as Nocky Salt. I thank God that this coarse and demeaning nickname was never attached to me. However I did not completely avoid a nickname. As you may know or not know, there is a very famous brand of health salts called Eno's Salts, which have the effect of toning up the system and cleaning out the bowels. Somehow my fellow pupils at the council school where I was educated connected me with this patent medicine and, to tell the truth, as I was a weakly child, they made my life hell at times. But all that was more than forty years ago, and in adult life having a similar name to a popular emetic only on very infrequent occasions causes any comment.

I am forty seven years of age, a tall, balding, thin man addicted to cigarette smoking. I mention this first because I have been warned by the doctors that if I don't give over I shall very likely die because of it. As an illustration of how addicted I am, it takes me three cigarettes and a double rum before I can stop coughing and get my breath in a morning. But sod them I say, you've got to die of something, and as I stand here by the gentlemen's conveniences looking up the Waterloo Road I feel very much alive. These public toilets are in the centre of the town and are the very axle of my life. I seem to have to come and stand here before I can ever make up my mind which way to go about my nightly business. There's a taxi rank, and an illuminated map of the town against the urinal, and each night as I begin my rounds, I stand against this and have a smoke before I start.

I am employed as a salesman. Perhaps a hawker or a pedlar would be a more appropriate name for what I do each evening. I collect a basket of sea food; prawns, cockles and mussels, kippers in bags, also black pudding, and I hawk these around the public houses of the town in much the same way that Molly Malone, the Irish girl in the old song used to do around the streets of Dublin. I very much doubt, however, that my ghost is likely to carry on doing it after I am dead as hers did, as I can't abide the job. In fact I hate it, and as soon as I can find employment more suitable to my talents, I shall chuck it in; but a living's a living and beggars can't buy forty fags a day, or afford a drink when they want one.

There are many reasons why I hate the job; having to wear a white linen jacket with 'SUPER COCKLES' printed on the back is one of them; this as can be imagined regularly produced lewd comments; I managed to get round it by wearing the jacket inside out, but having to wear a white American baseball cap with a big peak is to me the worst indignity of all. I feel such a fool when I've got it on. The younger men doing the same job put it on at what seems to me a jaunty angle and seem to enjoy wearing it, but mine fits low on my ears and makes me look an idiot. I asked the man who owns the business if I could perhaps wear a white trilby instead, but he wouldn't hear of it and laughed at my objections. I should have expected this reaction. The man's an ignorant pig who happens to have the Midas touch. They tell me he's worth a fortune and yet can't write his name. I call him a pig reluctantly as I made a resolution at New Year to stop calling people swine and pigs, at least not as often as I had been used to doing; but I can think of no other name that suits him, and it is my belief that he instinctively realises that I am more intelligent than he is and resents it so much that he takes pleasure in my discomfiture of having to wear the hat. He actually suggested to me that I should wear the peak at the back and roared with laughter when he saw the flash of anger on my face.

When I think of it I despair. How is it that I a man who has done courses at the local W.E.A. in many subjects and has had a poem published in the local newspaper, and all my life since I left school have been a member of the public library, sometimes reading two books a week, one of them non fiction, how is it that I am a poor man, and a dolt like the man that employs me, a man as thick as pigshit, makes a fortune. You must excuse my language but I feel so bitter that only strong language expresses the depth of my emotion, and any way it would be impossible to give any real sense of the world I intend to write about without using the rough language of the street. I often expressed this view to the Lecturer in English Literature at the W.E.A. classes I attended, but she didn't agree with me and I put this down to her genteel middle class background. When I asked what the words were for the basic bodily function, which surely are a natural part of human reality, she declined to pursue the argument.

But I digress. It is sufficient to say that I have always taken great pleasure in words and regularly came out somewhere near the top of my class at school for reciting poetry, a gift which unfortunately, in the level of life, and the part of the world that I live in has no meaning. Certainly, in none of the many jobs I have done has it been of the slightest value to me! Sometimes even my use of slightly flowery phrases has brought me into some ridicule from fellow employees; but as I stand here this night, with my ridiculous hat on, looking up the Waterloo Road, I often see the street lights as garlands and the clouds as wild horses, and before I begin my nightly round of the pubs, I light another cigarette and stand and let this view of the road with its garlands of street lights sink deep into my mind.

A few years ago, this town was in my opinion the best little drinking town in England. Nowhere had a more varied pub life. Every few yards there was a pub, and such names they had, all within an area no bigger than a couple of football fields. There was a Queens Head, a Duke William, a Marquis of Granby, an Old Crown, a Black Lion, a Red Lion, a Leopard, a Dolphin, a Sea Lion, a Roe Buck, a Unicorn, a Stags Head, a Durham Ox, a Bulls Vaults, a Millstone, a Huntsman, a Vine and a Foaming Quart, and last but not least, the drinking dens of the demi monde, the Jig Post, the Hole in the Wall and the Star, called the Star of Bethlehem. There were more than these but it would be a bore to write them all down. The town was a hive of pubs, each one a spitting distance from the next and they all seemed to be flourishing. The Star, where many of the lowest of the low did their drinking was always full. Mrs Potts, a vast fat woman never missed a night in the snug where she'd sit chommelling roast pork sandwiches and swilling them down her great gut with Guinness while her daughter, who is known as Beetroot, herself as big as a Sumo Wrestler, was usually propping up the bar, while her fancy man Stan, sat by the stove pot trying to work out where the next half pint was coming from.

I am told that this couple, who had at that time a big family of young children, somehow got the money together to go to the Costa Brava, as is the fashion these days, even among the unemployed members of the underclass. Anyway, while they were in Spain, Beetroot was seen on the beach trying to get her fat body into a bikini but I am told she could only just get one leg in the flimsy garment and in a fury she threw the bikini in the sea.

Every pub in the town had seedy characters and all were known to each other. It was a great fraternity of drink with it's own vertical class system, with the great Popes of booze at the very top; men who had usually reared big families without ever becoming defeated by it; men whose natural cunning was more than equal to the challenge of how to drink, smoke and even gamble every day on the meagrest of means. Such men were greatly looked up to by other lesser men who wished to do the same but hadn't the wit to manage it. Such great boozers as these were prized by publicans and their seats in the tap rooms were kept waiting for them.

There were all levels of pub life, from these highest down to

the lowly hangers on who were mere errand runners, men
without pride, tappers up, pikers, monstinks and a few real
nutcases. There were also decent family men who crept in just
before closing time for the odd half pint, and stood and marvelled
at the five pint a night men and wondered whether they'd done
the right thing in getting married, and giving up their freedom
for the world of napkins and rashes on babies arses. All these
various types of men made up the world I have lived my life in.

My own marriage failed but won't go into that; sufficient to
say that I must attend to a bar each night. The glittering spirit
bottles and the beer pumps are like an altar to me and the
barman or barmaid are priests. That is why I find this miserable
job I do bearable. At least it keeps me in nightly touch with all
the bars and smoke rooms of this town. In this world I am known
and know everybody. It is a cocoon where two miles away is alien
territory, a place where regularly on Saturday nights you can feel
the ghosts of dead men trying to get back to the camaraderie of
the pubs they used when they were knocking up and down in the
full flesh of their lives.

All pleasures were catered for here. Once there was a
wooden theatre called the Hippodrome, where as a child I saw
such diverse acts as Chinese acrobats spinning plates, a wild
donkey and a strong man lifting cartwheels. When the building
burned down the main road was black with swarms of rats
escaping from the fire.

There were also four cinemas, The Globe, the Ritz, the
Colloseum and the Palladium each changing its programmes
twice a week. There was a Billiards Hall, and there were many
chip shops, the mention of which brings me to the central theme
of my tale of the rise and fall of Sissymints, the finest chip shop I
ever knew, a little gold-mine if there ever was one and what's
more, much much more, is the fact, and it is a fact, that if
everybody had their own in this world, that chip shop should by
rights have been mine. But as you may have observed yourself,
that does not always occur in this world and like many others of
much higher stations in life than mine, I was robbed out of my
rightful inheritance, not I may say by the cunning machinations
of any other human being, but by the twist and turn of
circumstance that did not go my way.

So when I stand here against the lavatories looking down
the main Waterloo Road, and see the bright lights of the chip
shop that should have been mine, I feel the full weight of my
basket of sea food and when I catch a glimpse of myself in some
reflective surface wearing this damned silly hat, a sense of

bitterness at the miserable fate that deprived me of the dignity of being a business man in my own right and not an employee of an ignorant pig of a man comes over me, and I have to pull myself together and get on with my life as it is. "What can't be cured must be endured", is the little jingle I usually mutter to myself as I pass the window of the chip shop that should have been mine.

In the matter of chip shops I am something of an expert, having been a chip addict for most of my life. There is hardly a day that passes that I don't indulge myself in them and in my time I have seen (I was going to say hundreds, but on second thoughts I'll leave it at dozens), of chip shops rise and come to their full pomp and then fade away and die, and I have seen a few take deep root and prosper to such an extent that their owners have installed managers and gone to live on the Costa Brava or some similar place on the proceeds. This arrangement usually comes to grief as the manager of chip shops, whose owners are in foreign parts, are faced with such temptation to dip into the till that it would require people of superhuman integrity not to succumb. In my experience there are not a lot of these paragons about, at least not round these parts, but for all this most of the streets round here have got a chip shop, and chips have always been a fundamental part of working class diet. I have read, that the battle of Waterloo was was won on the playing fields of Eton. Well, I'll wager that if there were chip shops then, and I'm not sure if there was or wasn't that the battle was just as well won in the chip shops of that time. I am certain that the wars of this century were certainly won by legions of working class men raised largely on chips. This definitely would be true of men from this district, although I am prepared to acknowledge that chips may not play such a big part in the diet of the middle class as they do around here. I cannot imagine for instance that planning permission would be given for a chip shop in any of the big squares in London.

I sometimes have amused myself by phantasizing that Christopher Robin opened a chip shop in Grosvener Square, and incurred the wrath of the residents, but hereabouts there's no escape, and none wanted from chips. Generations of working class girls, who have hardly left school before they are married and big with child, rely almost totally on the chip pan to help them through the difficult child rearing years. Indeed I think that in such places as this, there should be a monument erected with an effigy of a single chip on top of it, and perhaps a companion monument, the pea, alongside it to give proper honour to a simple food made from humble ingredients, yet capable of giving the most ravishing of smells. But when I have mentioned this to members of the council they look at me as though I am off my twig; but then they are mostly men of little or no imagination.

Once I had a brain wave. It was at the time of the yearly Carnival and I was very disappointed at the turn out. There were a few floats, a tug of war between the local pubs and a lot of collecting boxes and that was it. As I stood watching this pathetic little procession, I remembered seeing a film of a religious procession in Spain where men carried a statue of the Virgin through the streets. The whole province turned out, thousands of them, swaying and chanting to the hypnotic beat of a big drum and it came to me like a flash that, with a little imagination, we could have the same thing here. Just imagine, a procession in honour of the chip and the pea with plaster images of both carried on floats through the city, and perhaps we could honour the tea pot as well while we were at it. The image of the chip could be carried on the shoulders of men of the chip frying fraternity; a guild could be formed in the same way that medieval guilds were formed by men associated with some trade or profession, and at each festival there could be a judging of the of the chip and chip shops, and prizes given. A great silver cup such as is given to football teams could be awarded each year. Such honour it would bring to the winners; their chip shops would turn into little gold-mines overnight. The Chip and Pea Grand Prix it could be called. After this brainwave came to my head, I could hardly sleep for thinking of the possibilities. I was convinced that it would put this little town on the map; but when I approached Councillor McYernanny about it, he looked uncomprehendingly at me as though I was speaking Hindustani.

His reaction was perhaps to be expected as he was the Councillor who once put forward the suggestion that water and gas could come down the same pipe and save the ratepayers a fortune. I had known Councillor McYernanny all my life. As a matter of fact we'd been in the same class at school and once we'd actually sat at the same desk. He'd tried to copy from me and offered me toffees to tell him the answers to sums. His mother made herb beer and treacle toffee which she sold from her back door on Sundays, but I digress as I often do. I think that my inability to stick to one theme has been my undoing; it's been the same with jobs. I've had dozens, some good, some bad but I've always got fed up with 'em and either walked out or got the sack.

"Keep sawing wood lad", my father used to say to me; but I

could never stick anything long. I read somewhere in Shakespeare, not that I read much Shakespeare. I've tried, but he seems to say things back to front if you know what I mean. Anyway I read that he said, "Only to thine own self be true, then thou can'st not be false to any man". Well it sounds all right, but as far as I'm concerned, it's impossible, as I seem to have a hundred different selves at the back of my eyes. I'm never the same man two days running. I can never make my mind up about anything, except things or people I don't like. Take this job for instance; I've made my mind up about that all right; and as soon as I can see my way clear I'll tell him where to stick his cockles and mussels and bloody silly cap. But I must be careful not to wallow in self pity; I don't mind indulging in a bit of it, but it soon gets to be a habit.

Mrs. Stott, the Lecturer at the W.E.A. was right when she said my brain could have done with a lot more education. There's a lot of folks round here as think they know a lot, but they don't know nothing. There's a lot of 'em never read a book in their lives yet to hear 'em talk you'd think they'd read the Encyclopedia Britannica. There's a pompous bugger as works in the Post Office. He always looks down at me and tries to talk posh and folks are taken in by it. They're as dumb as duckmuck some folks are. There's another bloke as drinks in the smoke room of the Old Crown they call Educated Evans. He's worked in a pit all his life and is filled with trick questions. I once heard him try to speak the Lord's Prayer backwards. It was nothing but a jumble but the daft buggers in the smoke room clapped him when he'd finished. They think he's clever. In my opinion it shows how ignorant they are, but to get back to the reason why I'm writing this.

I once tried to read "The Decline and Fall of the Roman Empire" by Gibbon though I'll be honest and confess I didn't get very far. But one thing it did; the title clicked and caused me to think about Sissymints, the chip shop that should have been mine. One night as I was lying in bed it came to me as I must write the history of the decline and fall of a chip shop. Not that Sissymints has completely declined, except that it isn't called Sissymints anymore, and my family, the Salts, don't own it, and in that respect as far as I'm concerned it can be said to have declined. But it's still there in Waterloo Road, still a chip shop firing on all cylinders every night, making somebody else a packet; but its great days, when it was the centre of the best drinking town in England are over.

The coming of television and closing of all those cinemas in the street directly opposite reduced it to being a ordinary chip shop. In its heyday, at night after the picture palaces closed, there were queues a hundred yards long and regularly fights broke out in the queues, while inside behind the counter there were half a dozen assistants sweating and serving as fast as the chips were fried, and upstairs in the dining room near pandemonium would be let loose as a poor moon faced youth carried trays of food to the hungry mob beating on the tables with salt cellars and vinegar bottles. Such were the great days and nights at Sissymints, and the memory of how it was is so strong in my mind, that I resolved to give such an institution its proper due and to write its whole history, from the first chip to the last.

Chapter One

A lot of what I write about in the early history of Sissymints occurred before I was born, but I have heard my father and mother speak about it and picked up bits and pieces of information from other sources. I have also used my imagination to provide the glue that sticks it all together. I have always had a vivid imagination and even knew what places were going to look like before I visited them. It was the same with people. I was hardly ever surprised by anything they did; in my mind's eye I could see happenings that occurred before I was born. It was this faculty that first caused me to consider this account. But I must also give credit to Miss Stott the Lecturer at the W.E.A., who, when I mentioned that I was going to attempt this history, was beside herself with excitement. She at once put me in contact with a Miss Eunice Threapwood, a lady who worked in the reference library, a middle aged spinster who had been in her time a fine figure of a woman, and in her top half still was, and knew it. She was also very knowledgeable about local history and found me many useful references, showing such zeal that I began to think she fancied me. She certainly often had the top button of her blouse undone as she bent over the table pointing out some item or other she thought might be useful to me. I began to call her the Luscious Librarian, but I digress and must stop it at once and get back to the main stem of my story.

It was Grandfather Saml, short for Samuel, Salt that I will begin with. He was the first man in my family to have anything to do with chips as most of the other male members worked down in the pit. Indeed his father Enoch Salt started in the coalmine at nine years of age, and one of his brothers named Cornelius Salt was killed by a fall of dirt in the pit on his seventeenth birthday. Samuel Salt somehow avoided this drudgery and got himself a pony and cart and earned his living by selling block salt and step whitener to folks in outlying districts, mainly in the Moorlands in the North of the Country. I am told he was a little man with a nose like a hook and a raw skewering voice to go with it. He was known as a "Hard boiled Hegg" who spat as he spoke and made no account of other folks' feelings. It is, I realise, something of a coincidence that he was named Salt and sold salt for a living. It may have been his being named Salt that had something to do with choosing salt to sell; and though I doubt it, such coincidences sometimes do occur in life.

On the back of his little cart his name Samuel had been abbreviated to Saml. As was the custom in the class of people he

lived among, and he was always known as Saml hereabouts. His
wife, my grandmother, was named Poll and they had nine
children. My father was the oldest son, and somehow, God only
knows how, the little pony and cart reared the lot of them
without them ever being any poorer than anyone else who lived
in their street, which was known at that time as Skinners Row,
and backed on to the canal at the back of his coal house. Saml
also had a collection of scrap which was mostly rubbish with odd
pieces of rusty iron amongst it. He always reckoned he could
make a pile out of scrap metal if he could just get a bigger cart,
as on his trips around the country lanes calling at lonely farm
houses he often came across pieces of scrap iron. Once he'd
managed to get an old mangle on the back of his cart and the
poor pony had mauled it back to the town where it stood for years
in the outhouse.

He was also a man who liked a drink and if he could afford
it a number of drinks. On the odd occasions he got drunk my
grandmother would scream that he was no more than a rag
tatter, and lock him out of the house. Then he'd sleep in the
outhouse with his head resting on the mangle, and when this
happened he sometimes sang "Ben Bolt" at the top of his voice to
defy her. This was the only song he ever sang and us children
often joined in to mock him. On one occasion he threw an iron
foot he used to mend the family's shoes with through the window.
My Grandma fetched the bobby to him, but usually they got on
well enough together compared to their next door neighbours
who fought like cat and dog every weekend.

Saml sometimes, when maudlin in drink, would bring my
grandmother a bottle of Guinness from the pub and make a fuss
of her, and she'd call him a daft old bugger, and then he'd start
on about her being only as thick as a strip lath when he married
her, and as how she'd eaten him out of house and harbour, and
now was a fat as an old sow pig, and as how he'd only got to
throw his trousers on the bed to get her in the family way. This,
for all it's rawness, was affectionate banter and the house on
such occasions was happy; that's if there was food in the pantry
and a copper or two in the teapot. But when times were bad, the
house could turn into a hell hole and Poll would scorp at him,
and call him for all the idle buggers she could lay her tongue to.

"I'd rather have a drunken man than an idle man", she'd
shout and start on about his selling his pony and getting a right
job labouring. When this happened he'd usually get his coat on,
and without saying a word go down to where he stabled his pony
and sit smoking and talking to it, and wouldn't come back to the

house all night. Next morning, my grandmother would send one of the children down to fetch the silly old bugger back in the house again.

Sometime he earned a few shillings by flitting people down one street to another, but money was always scarce. Poll often said the house they lived in was unlucky, as her mother had always drilled in her when she'd been a girl, "Never live in a house that faces the same direction as the workhouse". This would make my grandad mad as he said it didn't; then she'd say it did, and even though he'd proved her wrong she'd argue about it again and again, as she regularly brought the workhouse up to frighten him, and to tell the truth there were times when it seemed the whole family would end up there. To make it worse, Poll's eldest brother, Walter, a tall thin pathetic phlegm filled creature, crippled with arthritis, who'd been in the workhouse for years, often came to visit us in his workhouse suit which shamed Poll to death.

But for all this my grandmother was a strong woman who made a better job of her circumstances than many other women would and took pleasure in having her children round her. She'd even sing when doing the washing and cleaning the old range grate and could make a tasty meal out of the scrappiest of ingredients. Every week she'd make lobby in a dolly tub and it would last them all from Monday to Friday. Saml., when he was on his rounds in the country, would regularly get vegetable given him for nothing, and for a few pence on Saturday nights, as the meat market was closing, Poll would go round the stalls with a couple of her younger children. For no more than sixpence she'd get some kind-hearted butcher to fill her bag with scragg ends of meat which with the vegetables could make a stew to fill their bellies, and when the children got fed up with that stew, she'd use the fat from the meat to make chips in a chip pan. These were a great favourite with the children, and they'd have them at least once a day and occasionally, when there was money in the house, they'd go to the chip shop in the next street kept by a Mrs. Millie Ginders, and buy chip shop chips from her shop which was in her front parlour.

It was the proprietor of this shop that set the seed in Poll's mind that generations later became the Chip Emporium known as Sissymints, but at the time I'm writing of, this seed had not yet been planted, as it required a peculiar coincidence of circumstances for it to happen. One summer's day Saml. was sitting on his cart passing through a mining village a few miles from the town when he began to smell something burning, and as he sniffed the smell got stronger. Then as he came out into the centre of the village he saw the cause. Directly opposite a stone pub called the Lump of Coal, there had been a wooden hut that was a chip shop, but now it was only a smouldering ruin and sitting staring at it was a man named Albert Scragg who he knew to be the owner, as he had regularly sold him salt. He made his way towards him and as he got off his cart, Scragg turned his head and Saml saw his face was blackened with smoke and his eyes were wild with anger.

"I'll get him, I'll get the swine," he spat out, his voice filled with hatred. Then he started chuntering to himself about somebody called Amby. Saml could see he was off his head with rage so he began to poke about in the smouldering ruins of the chip shop, and with the toe of his boot, he kicked an iron bracket out that he first thought was a lever of some kind but as he leant down he recognised an iron chip cutter similar to the one he'd seen in another chip shop. As he stared at it, little did he realise that he was looking at the seed of his family's fortune, the key to a little gold mine.

By now Albert Scragg was standing up, and when Saml asked him how much he wanted for the bits of iron, Scragg didn't answer; instead he beckoned Saml to follow him in the direction of the Lump of Coal. Saml often used this pub on his travels and was well known to the regulars who were mostly colliers, and as he ordered his drink he was greeted by the landlord.

"How go Saml," he said as he pulled the beer then nodded toward Albert Scragg. The chatter in the bar went quiet as the men who were drinking round the scrubbed table by the stove pot looked uneasily at the owner of the burnt out chip shop who stared defiantly as the lot of them.

"I'll get the swine, don't you worry; I'll swing for him."

The publican who was known as Jacker at once butted in. "We'll have none of that talk in here, Albert. It's nowt to do with us, it's between you and him. Don't bring yer troubles here."

He was known as a strict publican who never had troubles in his pub and in the past had ordered many men out. So still glowering at the company, Albert Scragg sat down and Saml sat with him still trying to get a price for the bits of scrap iron. But in the next hour all Scragg could talk about was revenge on the man who'd burnt his chip shop down. He was sure it was a man named Ambrose Plant as there was bad blood between their families and had been for generations. This was a landscape of feud and litigations, a place of small one egg farms each surrounded by stone walls where territory was jealously guarded.

If there was any trespass by man or animal it often caused trouble, and these troubles sometimes lasted for generations. Between the Scraggs and Plants there'd been a feud going on for years that had started over a drain, and recently had been fuelled by a girl named Iris Plant who was very well made in the bust but simple in the head. She said she'd been felt at by a bus conductor on a bus called the "Flying Fox" which plied an hourly service to the town.

This bus was the first bus with pneumatic tyres, and the bus conductor she accused was a bit of a local dandy named Syd Baddely. He wore a slim pencilled moustache and fancied himself in his conductor's uniform, and was related to the Scragg family. This caused the feud to flare up again, and not long after, one of the Plants came into the chip shop and according to Albert Scragg, when his back was turned, Planty had spit a chew of tobacco in a fry of chips. He'd no evidence to prove this but he didn't need any, nor did he need any when his chip shop was set on fire. He knew the swine that had done it, and he sat pouring his bitterness out to Saml. There was no reasoning with him; he was unhinged with hate and would have hung the whole Plant family himself, women, babies the lot if it had been possible, as he reckoned they were no good, the lot of 'em

Old woman Plant was nicknamed Minny Knicknock and Albert reckoned she was mad. He said she burnt haystacks down and poisoned pigs. As he rambled on he was so filled with hatred that Saml couldn't get a price for the scrap metal out of him, and they both drank pint after pint till closing time when Jacker the publican turned them out. By now they were three parts drunk, and when they got back to the remains of the wooden chip shop some lads were dragging pieces of the smouldering wood across the field and Saml's pony and cart were nowhere to be seen.

He staggered across to the lads, "Have you seen me horse and cart?" he asked and one of them pointed in the direction of the main road. He hurried back and found his horse in the front drive of a big house eating the flowers in the garden. As best he could, without making any noise, hoping against hope nobody had seen the horse, he carefully backed out of the garden, got on the cart and began to make his way back toward the town: but before long the heat of the day and the gentle movement of the cart and the drink inside him caused him to doze off. He had often been in this state before and the horse knew it's way home. By the time it turned into the street where he lived, he'd fallen into a drunken sleep and was wakened by his eldest boy, my father Len, shaking him. Then he saw Poll standing at the back door with a face clenched like a fist and shouting that he was a drunken bugger and could sleep with the horse. He began unharnessing the pony and as he did he noticed something on the back of the cart. Looking closer he saw that it was the old iron chip cutting machine covered in grey ash.

How the hell did that get on here? he asked himself; then he remembered the lads dragging the charred wood in the field and reckoned that it must have been them that put it there. "The little sods," he cursed, lifting it up. He dropped it down by the mangle and resolved to take it back whenever he was passing that way again, but he never did. Somehow or other he always forgot, and as month after month passed and he saw nothing of Albert Scragg, it got pushed to the back of his mind, and that was how the family of Salts began in the chip frying business. But the seed had not sprouted yet and for the next few years it mouldered away in the outhouse while the world outside was beginning to change

Not that it wasn't changing all the time, but the changes were becoming more noticeable. There were more motors in the streets and a regular bus service ran through the city. The town at night seemed brighter lit and the Council had capped it all by having new Public Lavatories built underground on the corner of Queen Street. For the best part of a year there had been scaffolding round the site and the district was filled with rumours about the wonder of these new conveniences. This was at a time when most of the street houses had only earth closets, and many people had never used a flush toilet and couldn't imagine what it felt like to use one. Some of the older folks didn't hold with it as some of them were afeared they would be sucked down into the drain pipe by the force of the flush. For months there was talk about closets in the public houses, some of it ribald, as there was to be a great opening ceremony. It was said that Lord Derby, the greatest peer in the land was to cut a ribbon and then have a pee in one of the stalls and if he felt like it, sit on one of the closets and christen it. As the great day approached, the Council decorated the road with bunting and a Union Jack was hung on a flagpole sticking out from the upstairs window of the Queens Hotel.

The opening ceremony was to be performed on a Saturday, but unfortunately it was pouring with rain and the flags and bunting hung soaked and limp. The bandsmen from the Co-op Band were soaked and limp as well, and their instruments were soaking wet in their hands and the sounds they made were wet and muffled. Everybody who'd come to watch the ceremony huddled close to the buildings hoping for shelter there, but there was none. All the schoolchildren in their wet clothes stood shivering and cold, while the awning on the platform where the worthies stood kept flopping up and down. Then as the Lord Mayor began to to speak, the wind blew the awning up and tipped water over his wife who was standing by a big fat man who everybody assumed must be Lord Derby. They later discovered that the speaker was Mr. Pickersgill the boss of the Civil Works Dept., as Lord Derby had, it turned out, sent a message saying he was indisposed. So after the Lady Mayoress had been helped, dripping, off the platform, the Lord Mayor cut the ribbon at the entrance of the gentlemen's urinal and Mr. Joseph Pickersgill had the honour of being the first man to actually pee there. When he reappeared at the top of the step there was a great cheer from a group of customers looking from the window of the tap room of the Queens Hotel. Among them, with a rose in his buttonhole was Saml. Salt, who, for the rest of his life claimed that he had been one of the first to use the gentlemen's urinal.

For the next few weeks thousands of folks went down the steps to view and then use this marvel of the modern age. Some came from the country and had no idea what a flush toilet was. A few even had no idea of how the simple ratchet locked on the lavatory doors. One woman, a Mrs. Ada Swingwood got herself locked in as she couldn't pull the latch across with her old rhumaticky fingers, and began to scream. There were others less modest who sat on the closet with the doors open as though they were in their own backyards, but all in all the general opinion was that the lavatories were a great step forward into the modern age.

There were of course a few dissenters, mostly on religious grounds who reckoned that such a public show of bowel functioning was immoral and would lead to a collapse of civilised values. One Sunday-school master actually preached from the pulpit that the lavatories were the devil's work and that he wouldn't go down into their sink of iniquity if they gave him a thousand pounds. But after a month or two when the novelty had worn off, life returned to normal and the lavatories no longer featured in people's conversations. There was one flare up though that was reported in the local paper; a Councillor from a ward in the southern part of the city, jealous no doubt that the lavatories were not in his area, complained that the lavatory attendants were related distantly to certain councillors and that he had proof the short lists for the jobs were dummy runs and the jobs had already been fixed. This led to bitter exchanges, and one Councillor took his jacket off in the Council chambers, adopted a fighting stance and asked the accuser to come outside. But as tempers subsided the fuss blew over.

All this occurred in the month of July, in the same month the greater world outside had also been experiencing difficulties. The Kaiser had been making threatening noises and other European nations were becoming alarmed. The whole of the European continent was becoming restless. There was a madness in the blood, and somewhere in Saragevo, a place nobody in our town had ever heard of, the Archduke Ferdinand was putting his feathered hat on and preparing for a procession, while somewhere close by a man named Princip was putting bullets in a revolver. Not long after one of the bullets blew out the brains of the archduke and Europe was ready to bathe in it's own blood. On the front page of the local paper the Kaiser and the Germans began to be written about as enemies, and young men joining up were having their photographs taken.

Back in Stringer Street, at first there wasn't much of a reaction to these happening; things had gone on in the same way for so long that nobody could imagine life any different than it was. There was a sense of patriotism among the better educated, but down the backs and in the tap rooms it took longer to penetrate. When the denizens of these places did finally realise that the conflagration was likely to include them, and that there was a chance their lives could be completely changed, some took fright and found good reasons why they couldn't join up.

Saml Salt being in his late forties was too old, but being a strong conservative in politics, he made great play of patriotism and so influenced his two younger sons who were now in their teens that they both made their way to the recruiting office and listed in the Army. My father Len, the oldest, was working in the pit and all colliers were exempt, but the two younger brothers going caused Poll great unhappiness as they were both in work and their contributions to the household budget had made life much easier. When Saml realised what they were about to do and it's consequences, he begged and pleaded with them to get a job in the pit or stay at home but it was no use. Billy was courting at the time and wanted to show himself a brave Englishman to his young woman, so he went to the recruiting office on the Monday and was passed fit. This so excited his younger brother Charlie, that he went two days later and did the same.

Neither of them told their father or mother that they were going till they'd done it. When they did Poll started to wail like an animal in pain. It was a terrible sound to hear. Saml had never seen her cry before, but her face was soon wet with tears and as he stood helplessly watching her heave and then snort, he thought she was going to have a stroke. Then suddenly, she stopped and began to put tongue to him. It was all his fault. She called him all the bloody fools God ever made. It was him as should a'gone. It would have been the best end of him. They should kill the old 'uns off first. Then she brought the workhouse up again. What were they going to live on when the lads had gone? She'd reared them from babies and as soon as they were bringing a shilling or two in, the King and Country wanted 'em. What had King and Country ever done for her with a houseful of kids to rear. It 'erd be the best thing if the Germans did come; it wouldna be any worse than it was nar; they are all the same.

"Sometimes I think we'd all be better off in the churchyard," she stormed. Saml had to listen to this sort of talk for days after the lads had gone and it was true that times were getting harder. Grocers shops were selling table salt in packets that you could pour out and the block salt trade was finished. Most days he was up and down the streets of the town with his horse and cart hoping to drop on a flitting job, or sometimes he'd fetch a bag of coal from the coalyard. But these little jobs didn't come very often and some days there was nothing doing at all and, as he passed pubs he'd often had a drink in, there was great bitterness in his heart. He hadn't a penny in his pocket, and he cursed blindly whatever or whoever was responsible for his sad condition. Then one day, not long after the lads had joined up, his luck changed. He didn't recognise it at the time but as they say every dog has his day. Saml had always thought his day had come and gone and he'd never even noticed it. But he was wrong.

Chapter Two

It was a hot sultry morning and Saml was sitting in his
empty cart watching his horse's tail and wondering where the
next job was coming from and whether he'd ever have enough
money in his pocket again to sit in a tap room and enjoy a pint
when he heard a voice shouting, "Mr. Salt, Mr. Salt." It was Mrs.
Ginders standing at the door of her chip shop beckoning him, so
he turned his horse across the road thinking perhaps she wanted
something moving; but when he got off the cart he saw she was
very agitated.

"It's Kronjie, he's bad, I can't move him. I wonder if you'd
mind giving me a hand." Kronjie Ginders was her husband, a
long thin bone of a man, crippled with rheumatism, who spent
most of his days peeling potatoes in the back room of the chip
shop. How he'd come to get the nickname Kronjie nobody knows,
not even him, but somehow it suited him perfectly. Saml had
known him all his life, but when he followed her into the back
room of the shop, which was the kitchen, he had a shock, for
Kronjie was lying sprawled out half on and half off a chair with a
dribble of spit coming out of his mouth and all his face somehow
askew.

"He's been like this since Sunday. It's his throat. I've given
him some lemon tea but he can't keep it down,' Mrs. Ginders said
as she stood staring down at her helpless husband. It was
immediately apparent to Saml that Kronjie had had a stroke.

"A stroke?" She repeated the word as though she'd never
heard it before and they stood staring at him. Kronjie groaned
and slipped forward off the chair, his long body crumpling down
on the coconut matting. At once they both tried to maul him up
again, but as they did, a strangulated whistling sound came from
his throat as though he was choking so they let him slip back on
the mat.

"We shall have ter get somebody else to help us. He's very
bad Missus. I should get the doctor." In those days folks hardly
ever saw a doctor. It was probable Kronjie had never seen one in
his life and Mrs. Ginders looked shocked at the word, repeating it
incredulously, "Doctor . . . . . Doctor."

"I'll make some more lemon tea if we can just get him up.
He'll be all right; it's his throat."

"His throat woman?" Saml shouted at her. "He's bad this
man is." And as he said this Kronjie seemed to go into some sort
of spasm. He drew one of his legs suddenly up and his whole
body began to twitch. His head twisted sideways and his tongue

blocked his mouth and a gurgling noise came from him. Then suddenly he slackened and all the locked tensions fell away from him. His head slumped sideways and his grizzled cheek rested flat on the coconut matting.

"He's a gonner," Saml said. "He's gone dead."

"Dead . . . . . Kronjie . . . . . Kronjie," she shouted, getting down on her knees. "He inna dead, feel at him . . . . . Kronjie," she shouted down at him.

Saml shook his head. "He's dead Mrs Ginders; that was the death rattle as come from him; I've heard it before."

"He's still warm, feel at him." Her eyes were wide with panic; she felt under her husband's shirt at his heart.

"He'll be warm for hours yet Missus, you'd better fetch the doctor. He can do no good but he'll have ter see him."

The truth that her husband was dead was now being slowly accepted by her. "Whatever am I going to do, I can't run this place without him," she cried.

Well he can't help yer now Missus; he's past helping any body. You'll have ter get the doctor or the bobby."

This did not seem to register and she kept bleating, "I don't know what I'm going to do; how shall I manage. I shall have to shut the shop."

Saml realised she was past being able to think clearly so he decided to go for the bobby himself.

This was the beginning of the Salt family's association with chip shops. From that chance meeting, the seed began to grow. Mrs. Ginders was helpless without her husband. Saml found out they hadn't even got a chip cutting machine. He remembered the one he had in the outhouse so he cleaned it up as best he could and offered to sell it to her, but the shock of her husband's death had unhinged her mind and she didn't seem to understand anything. Every time he attempted to talk to her, she stared blankly at him and kept thanking him for his help. "Yow bin pure gold ter me Mr. Salt. I dunner know what I'd a done without yer."

It was true that Saml had made most of the funeral arrangements for her. After she'd come back from the churchyard, they stood looking through the chip shop window and she asked him if he'd help her with peeling the potatoes. Saml agreed on condition that she bought the chip slicer from him, which she agreed to do. He fixed it to the back kitchen table and began to work in the chip shop. A few week later a girl called Lily Maddox, who'd had the sack from a pot bank happened to call in the shop and Mrs. Ginders gave her a part time job helping her to serve behind the counter. So it came about that the Salts began to get experience in the business of running a chip shop.

The life of the district by now, like life in the rest of the country was completely changed. There were men in Khaki everywhere. Billy came home on leave, smart in his uniform and filled with great tales about the doings of his regiment in France. He was in the Cavalry and said that they'd encountered a squad of Black Uhlans and engaged them in combat. He'd cut one of the German troopers down with his sabre and been praised by his commanding officer for his bravery. Saml didn't believe him for he knew Billy was a liar, and so it turned out, for he heard from another soldier that he'd seen Billy unloading horses in Belgium. He'd spoken to Billy so he knew it was him, as Billy had told him he was glad he'd dropped on a cushy number, and he'd rather see a horse's arse than Germans any day.

Charlie came home on leave, his arms covered in tattoos, and spent most of his leave boozing. He got into a fight with Gudger Gethin who was a labourer when he worked, and a bloody nuisance when he didn't, so he was banned from most of the local pubs for fighting. He was a thick set powerful man who liked to goad young soldiers, and Charlie, being proud as a peacock in his uniform and tattoos was a perfect target for this bully. They both met up in the bar of the Red Lion, about the only pub in the town that would still serve Gudger. One thing led to another, and Charlie thinking he was stronger than he was, told Gudger to get outside. Gudger obliged, and threw Charlie through the window of the Home and Colonial Stores. The police were called with the result that both were summonsed and fined.

This caused hell up. Poll shouted he'd brought disgrace on the family as none of the Salt family had ever been in the Police's hands before, but Saml just told him to keep off the drink. Charlie said "Listen who's talking". The row went on and on all day, until Charlie said he'd be glad to get back to the trenches. His father told him to bugger off back then, which he did. Poll was very upset when he'd gone and said it was all Saml's fault as usual.

There were now many wounded soldiers about and the newspaper were filled with casualty lists. A man from the next street who was in the Grenadier Guards won the V.C. His photo was on the front page of the local newspaper and there was a ceremony when he came home on leave. Colonel Blizzard led a parade in the park and Poll and her two youngest children went. By now all her family except two had left school and had found work of one sort or another, so there was money coming into the house each week. Poll said she'd never been better off in her life and if it wasn't for folks getting killed, wars were a good thing. Mrs. Ginders chip shop flourished and was open till twelve at night.

Then an accident in Stringer Street occurred that changed everything. A man they called Fat Fitz who worked as a grave digger and was reputed to be able to drink ten pints while the clock struck twelve, came home blind drunk one night and must have turned the gas on without lighting it. When he got up next morning and put a match to the fire, there was a terrible explosion which killed him, demolished his house, badly shook all the houses nearby and made Poll think the Germans had dropped a bomb.

Most of the roof tiles on Saml's house were dislodged and you could see the sky through the back bedroom ceiling. The house had always been bent with subsidence as the district was riddled with old mine workings and the landlord had only recently had a dowel rod fixed in place to hold the outside wall up. But when Poll approached him to have the roof replaced, he flatly refused and offered to sell her the house, as the four and threepence a week rent wasn't worth him having all the trouble and expense. Poll was bitter about this and at first refused to pay any rent. The landlord threatened to summons her, so Saml borrowed a ladder and tried to cover the holes in the roof himself. But as he'd never been on a roof before he found the job very difficult.

One day as he was coming down the ladder a stave broke and he fell to the ground breaking his arm and shaking him up very badly. Poll said he was never the same man after this accident. He couldn't do his job properly at the chip shop and for months he was up and down, a pale shadow of the man he used to be.

His horse had died a long time back and he'd sold his cart. As he sat in the corner under the back window he often reminisced about the times he'd had when selling salt in the moorland villages. When he shuffled across to Mrs. Ginders chip shop and did what he could, she used to say what a poor old soul he'd become, but for all his infirmities, they got on very well together, and Mrs. Ginders said she didn't know what she'd do without him, which was very strange as Poll couldn't abide the sight of him sitting around pulling his face at home. It seemed as though being in the chip shop cheered him up. There was always summat doing, with folks coming in and out, and as he'd always been used to being up and down on his cart it suited him better

than sitting staring at his own firegrate. Besides, Mrs. Ginders
was a cheerier woman than Poll.

The girl Lily Maddox got on so well with Mrs. Ginders she
often slept in the back bedroom of the shop and became like a
daughter to her. Both her and Saml now treated the chip shop as
their second home and this suited Mrs. Ginders as she suffered
badly with back ache and was a great believer in Sloane's
Liniment; but as she couldn't rub this on her back herself, she'd
get young Lily to do it. Then one day, when she'd got her corsets
off and Lily was rubbing the liniment on, Saml happened to
come in through the door and it seemed the most natural thing
in the world for him to have a go, and soon he'd taken the back
rubbing job over. There was no sexual involvement between
them as Saml always said he'd none of that feeling left; it had all
gone from him. "I've been dead down there years," he used to say
indicating his trousers, and so there was always the stink of
Sloane's Liniment in the shop, which, mixed with the frying
chips, made a strange and distinctive smell that some of the
customers even said they liked.

When Lily happened to tell Poll that Saml rubbed Mrs.
Ginders back, this became a great source of amusement to her
and she used to taunt him about it. "Her'll have thee rubbing
her chest next. They'd have ter get her to rub thee John Thomas
with it, see if it'll do any good." But there was no jealousy in
these remarks; they'd long since gone past anything of that sort
except as regards money as Poll was never sure how much Mrs.
Ginders paid Saml for his help and often went through his
trouser pockets when he was asleep.

Outside this little world of the few streets around the chip
shop and all the domestic concerns of the Salts the whole of
Europe had changed. The War was now over and there had been
a week of drunken celebration; Billy was soon to be demobbed;
Charlie was with his regiment in India; the Austro Hungarian
Empire was no more; Germany was bankrupt; there was trouble
in Ireland; the streets were filled with motor cars. They were
putting up a war memorial with all the names of the dead
soldiers on it in the square and when the statue was officially
unveiled at a big ceremony by the Lord Mayor, Saml noticed a
curious thing; the Lord Mayor was cross-eyed and so was the
Mace bearer. This coincidence tickled him so greatly that he
told every body he met about it till Poll was sick of hearing him
and said he was going funny in the head in his old age. It was
true they were both getting old. All their family had grown up
and had found their places in the world outside the family home.

Len, my father, who'd often done jobs at the chip shop his father couldn't manage, had met and courted Lily Maddox, and when they got married she was three months gone. So when she was brought to bed with twins she had to leave her job at Mrs. Ginders to stay at home and look after them. The twins incidentally were me and my sister Phoebe. This left her job empty at the chip shop and my Aunty Cissie Salt, who wasn't married and had never shown any interest in lads, started to work there and get on very well with Mrs. Ginders. The married daughters, Emmy, Lizzie and Dora brought their children back to their mother's so often that Saml said he wished they'd keep away as the children were a bloody nuisance. This caused Poll to say he was an unnatural man.

Mrs. Ginders was now practically helpless with arthritis; even Sloane's Liniment made no difference, and so the focus of attention of this little history must move away from that nineteen fourteen war generation and it's main protagonists Saml, Poll and Mrs. Ginders. It's sufficient to say that they all found their ends within eighteen months of each other. Saml and Poll went from this world without great difficulty as they had easy deaths — if death can ever be said to be easy. But Mrs. Ginders suffered a lot of pain and for the last twelve months of her life came to rely entirely on my Aunty Cissie who was as good as gold to her and attended to all her needs. For this she left her the shop, and so Aunty Cissie Salt became in her mid twenties a property owner, and the main character in this book.

Chapter Three

Saml had always said Cissie had her head screwed on. Some said she'd got it screwed on too tight. What was certain was that she was a hard working young woman who didn't want to live the life her parents had, "Scratin' and scrawning for every penny", as she put it. She was different from all her sisters who'd got married not long after they'd left school and begun to have families a few months later. She'd never gone out with young men nor shown any interest in 'em. It was as though she'd made up her mind that her life was going to be different from other wenches. Napkins and blarting babies were not for her. Not that she was a woman without feelings; she had come to have real affection for Mrs. Ginders and was very upset when she died even though she'd known the shop would be left to her. She'd been so upset she shut the shop for three days, and said for months after that she could feel the presence of Mrs. Ginders behind the counter. But she was also ambitious in her own way and had a number of plans for the business.

The first thing she did was to establish a regular connection with a fishmonger. There was a lot of difficulty doing this as the fish had to be fresh and the shop was in the Midlands. A daily supply was not always available. She also started to sell pop as the mineral water trade was rapidly developing. Then realising she couldn't run the concern herself, she became the employer of labour.

The first person she took on part time to help her behind the counter was a woman called Aunty Elsie who was no relation but for some reason that was what she was called. Her full name was Elsie Simcock and sometimes she was called Chopsy Simcock. Her husband had been killed in the pit and she had been left with three young children to rear, which she'd managed mostly by cleaning in pubs. She was a thin, fierce, hyper-thyroid woman with heavy breasts and bright glittering eyes. Her little shiny nose was like a beak and you could see into her nostrils as she talked to you. She had no teeth of her own and couldn't abide wearing her false teeth, so her cheeks had a sucked in appearance. But despite these features and the difficulties of her life she was always cheerful and greeted most customers who came into the shop with familiarity as she seemed to know by name everybody who lived or had lived in the surrounding streets. If by any chance she knew them well, no sooner had they stepped through the door than she'd begin a long crying sound "ehehhhn eeheeho!" as though she couldn't find proper words to

Cissie Salt

express her pleasure at seeing them and when this cry of recognition finally ran down she'd begin to gabble away ten to the dozen. Cissie often had to cut Elsie's gossip short so she could serve the other customers, but all in all she was a very valuable asset to the shop. She had enormous energy and would be in and out the back kitchen banging doors, carrying buckets, scrubbing floors on her knees from morning to midnight, and for a while the two of them managed to run the shop themselves.

Then after the boxes of fish began to be delivered it soon became evident that they needed a man to help for a few hours a day as Cissie found that touching the fish made her break out in black blotches. It was only when the fish was wet, but it became difficult when they were opening the fish boxes so Cissie got an old man to help them. His name was George Duckers who was called locally Judder. He was seventy years of age but still sprightly and in many ways he was just the man for the job except for one unfortunate habit. He was not particular about personal hygiene and after a while Cissie noticed he stank. At first she thought it was the fish or the tom cat that hung about the yard, but then she couldn't help noticing that his trousers round his crutch always seemed wet and she realised that he peed himself and it was that which was causing the stink. It was a difficult situation as she quite liked the old man and didn't want to hurt his feelings. Aunty Elsie had no such sensitivity and confronted him about it.

"Thee wants wear a baby's napkin," she said to him one morning as he was lugging a bag of potatoes into the shop. He turned on her his face contorted with rage. "You shit, Elsie," he spat out.

At once Elsie was on her dignity. "You dirty old devil, I've never been spoken to like that before. I'm not used ter that language." She then rushed back into the shop and told Cissie what he'd said and when Cissie confronted him with it, the shouting match between them started again. The outcome was that Elsie said it was either him or her that went and that was the end of poor old Judder at the chip shop. They had a number of men after that but none stayed long. One was caught pinching a bag of potatoes, another, a poor youth with blue lips who suffered with asthma couldn't lift the bag and Elsie had to help him. They finished with him after he had a bad asthma attack and his face turned blue and they had to fetch the doctor.

Cissie herself was beginning to suffer with bronchitis. She put it down to the coal dust that blew across the backs from a coal wharf. Sometimes when the wind was in a certain direction, the air was thick with it. It got into your eyes and caused your spit to be black. This, with the smell from a butchers slaughterhouse at the end of the street when mixed with the stink of the fish boxes often made Cissie feel sick.

Once when she went out into the back yard she nearly stepped on a rat, which so frightened her that she screamed and Elsie had to fetch a drop of brandy from the Travellers Rest, a pub in the next street. All this and the constant thrum, thrum from grinding machinery in the big grit mill nearby sometimes made her think of trying to make a move but it was only wishful thinking; she never did anything about it. Her nature was to stop where she was and keep on complaining.

At that time there was a restlessness in the town. Many men were on the dole. At every street corner there'd be a group of them standing and staring at nothing much, flipping their woodbines so as to have a smoke left in the afternoon and the talk was all of the picture palaces that had just been opened in a street just off the Waterloo Road. The Colloseum, that had been converted from a theatre, had a heavily ornate interior with gilt painted plush boxes for courting couples at the back. The Ritz next door to it had recently opened in a great fanfare of publicity, and directly facing the main road, the Palladium was showing Charlie Chaplin films. Each of the picture palaces changed the programme on Wednesday and all the talk in the street was of what was on next. Everybody that came into the chip shop was full of the last films they'd seen. Neither Cissie nor Elsie had any time to go as each night they were open till midnight, but Cissie was very curious as a number of her customers had said the films made them cry. So one afternoon she told Elsie to get her coat on and they shut the shop and went up to the town to the afternoon matinee at the Palladium.

They went in through the foyer feeling nervous. Elsie actually trembled as the swing doors opened and shut behind them and when they saw the vast interior with all the plush seats and enormous screen they were nonplussed for they'd no idea what a picture was or what a film on a screen would look like. Elsie still thought that real people would perform. The usherette who showed them to their seats was a girl named Nellie Washington from the street where Elsie lived. She had at times been in the chip shop so this helped to take the strangeness away as she led them to seats right in the middle of the cinema. As they were about to sit down, Elsie, who had never sat on tip up seat before, got her coat caught up in the tip up mechanism. This alarmed her and as she couldn't get it loose she began to panic and Nellie had to come with her torch to get the coat loose. A few minutes after this when the lights went down the first picture was flashed on the screen Elsie emitted her loud drawn out greetings cry "eehecheheeh!" Other folks sitting near to them shouted "ssh!" but Elsie who was not used to being shut up by anyone was so amazed at the image on the screen she couldn't stop and when the first film came on she kept on talking aloud. Cissie tried to shut her up but it was no good. Elsie didn't seem able to understand that what was happening on the screen was illusion. To her it was reality and she kept shouting out at the actors. This caused such irritation among people sitting near to them that one man stood up and said something about fetching the manager. Then Nellie the usherette came with her torch which caused further commotion and talk of people asking for their money back, so Elsie was forced to sit quiet, mumbling to herself. When the lights went up at the end of the show and they were filing out, the man who'd stood up and remonstrated about the noise must have said something to Elsie, for she turned savagely on him and shouted "Shut your chops, you. What's it got to do with you?"

The man, a tall bald headed fellow with spectacles, at once retaliated by making a gesture of dismissal. "I don't argue with ignorant people Missus," he said, putting his trilby hat on.

The word ignorant had an immediate effect on Elsie. "Ignorant am I?" she shouted at him, "I'm as good as you any day."

The man just stood and sneered at her. "I'm not arguing with you Missus, just get off home," he said with as much dignity as he could muster.

This seemed to enrage Elsie more than being called ignorant. "Get off home," she repeated, her chin trembling furiously. "Who the hell do you think you're talking to! You get off home yer bloody thing."

A group of people now stood listening and the woman behind the pay desk ran to a door with the word Manager on it. Seconds later a little bald man with frizzy hair over his ears and wearing a dress suit jacket and bow tie came out and stepped between the two antagonists.

"What seems to be the trouble Madam?" he said to Elsie seeing that she was the most agitated person there.

"It's that bloody article; he's called me ignorant. I'm not used to being spoken to like that by my own family. He's more ignorant than what I am."

The tall man in a trilby just stared at her, sneered and

turned away as though he'd decided she wasn't worth any more
of his attention and without more ado he walked through the
doors of the cinema and disappeared leaving Elsie and Cissie
among a little group of people who'd been watching the scene.
Cissie pulled Elsie toward the door.

"Come on Elsie, that's enough," she said. A look of relief
came over the manager's face and he smiled thankfully. But Elsie
wasn't done. Her dander was up and before she allowed herself to
be pulled away she shouted, "I've seen his sort before. I could shit
'em. Me ignorant huh! It's him as is ignorant, the bloody thing."

At this Cissie jerked her arm and got her through the door
and turned on her ferociously. "Elsie you've shamed me to death.
I'll never step in there again. Oh I've never been so ashamed in
my life; how could you in front of all them folks."

Elsie looked baffled at this attack from her employer. "It was
him as was ignorant, not me. I'm not standing that from
anybody."

Cissie, intent on her own shame ignored this. "I'll never step
foot in that place again. Oh I didn't know where to put my face,
all them people. It'll be all over the town."

Elsie face flushed defiantly, "I don't give a bugger what folks
think about me. It's what I think about them as matters."

The talk went on in this way as they walked through the
streets toward the chip shop. The wonder of the talking pictures
had been lost in the altercation and later Cissie said she thought
nothing of picture palaces as they were only shadows on a wall.
She never went to the pictures again.

As for Elsie I do not know whether she did or not as it was
not long after that she left the shop for a better job on a stall in
the covered market. I mention this episode in the cinema because
that was the first time the little street of three cinemas had
played any part in Cissie's life. Until then she'd no idea the place
could be of any particular significance to her. But a few days
later, somebody came into the chip shop at dinnertime and
mentioned that a little cafe and oatcake shop, directly opposite
the cinemas on the other side of the main road, was closing down
as the proprietor, a man known as Lanky Fred, was selling up.
This cafe had been open years and was the haunt of workmen of
all kinds in the morning and in the afternoon of boozers who'd
been in the pub till closing and were killing time till they opened
again at six o'clock. It was famous for its dripping sandwiches
and big mugs of tea and the filthy jokes of Lanky Fred who had a
stiff leg.

Cissie had once been in the cafe when she was a little girl

and clearly remembered Lanky Fred Potts, a man well known in the district for gambling. She recalled he'd asked her whose little wench she was and when she'd told him her name was Salt, he'd laughed aloud. "I thought yer featured a Salt. Are you one of Saml's wenches?" When she nodded that she was, he'd grinned. "Yer a little pinch of Salt are yer. Yer feature yer Fayther." All this came back to her as she was serving and for some strange reason she couldn't get the little shop out of her mind. Being called a pinch of salt had always stuck, and she'd used the expression many times in her life since. Then, sometime later, she overheard a conversation about how well a sweet and tobacco shop in Queen Street near the cinemas was doing since the picture palaces had opened. It had turned into a little gold-mine one person said.

She'd pricked her ears up at this. "A little gold-mine." She repeated the phrase to herself as she bent over a fry of chips. She was by now about thirty years of age and looked older, especially when the shop got hot. Her complexion had a yellowish tinge and her face often sweated a lot. She had never been a woman who'd troubled about her appearance. Her greatest comfort was money and by now she'd got a tidy bit put by, not a lot by local business standards but a fortune compared to what most of her neighbours in the nearby streets had and certainly by what her parents had been used to.

She was known locally as a tight-fisted woman. "There's plenty goes in but not much comes out a Cissie Salt's," was the sort of remark made about her. She was even mean to two of her younger married sisters who helped her in the shop, often deducting out of what she paid them the price of any fish and chips they took home; and this love of money was now showing in her face. Her mouth often clenched shut as she attended to the till as though she was hiding the amount she was putting in. These characteristics were fuelled by an ambition to make more and more and as she lay alone in her bed that night after hearing about the little gold-mine in Queen Street she was restless and couldn't sleep. Her mind kept making a connection between the scene in the cinema and the little shop opposite with the phrase about a gold-mine. Before morning it had come together as a decision to enquire further about Lanky Fred's shop.

There was no plan, no commitment. It would be just an idle enquiry out of curiosity she told herself and next morning in the cold light of day she almost changed her mind about going and even as she was putting her coat and hat on she was telling herself she was really going up to the Home and Colonial Stores to do a bit of shopping. But as she walked up the bank there was sense of excitement that she really couldn't explain as she knew quite well any idea of buying the shop was completely beyond yer means. But when she got to the meat markets, instead of going across the road to do her shopping she made toward Waterloo Road where the little shop was and sure enough there was a "For Sale" notice in the window.

Apply Duckmore & Pidbeard it said. They were the solicitors that had dealt with Mrs. Ginder's will and this somehow allayed her anxieties. She remembered clearly Mr. Tongue, the clerk who'd said she was a very lucky young woman when he'd read the will to her and how she'd been so excited that day as she'd sat trembling on the seat in front of the Cenotaph. All this came into her mind as she stood dithering in front of the shop window. Then almost in a trance she found herself walking in the direction of Riley Street at the back of the Town Hall where the solicitors' was. Their office was a corner terrace house. The door was open and as she went in who should be coming out but Mr. Tongue, a little pompous man with a gold watch chain, rimless spectacles and a head that was so completely bald it seemed as though it had never known what hair was.

As soon as he saw her he beamed a greeting. "Miss Salt, how very nice to see you. We've been hearing a lot about you; and what may I ask brings you here today?" She was at once flummoxed by him saying he'd heard a lot about her and muttered something about the shop for sale, which caused the expression on his face at once to become very thoughtful. And although he'd been on his way out, he stopped and ushered her into a small room against the stairs and in a moment he'd fetched a folder with all the particulars regarding the shop which he put out on the table in front of him and began to study them intently.

"It was very fortunate you caught me then my dear. I was on my way out to a sad matter. I'm afraid my client is not expected to last the week out. Oh dear, soliciting is often a painful business," he sighed. "But I hear you're becoming a successful business woman my dear. You know I always knew you would. I can always tell. We've got our ears to the ground in this office. It's all part of the job. We like to know what's going on in the town. These are exciting times my dear. The world it's changing fast. Sometimes I think a bit too fast, but we try to keep up. Now let me see. Oh yes! 23 Waterloo Road." He bent down over the table to study the contents of the folder more carefully then pulled a white starched handkerchief out out of his pocket and put it against his nose. Then he looked up at her. "These premises, my dear, offer a great opportunity. They are in no way developed to their full potential."

Half an hour later when she left the building she'd made a decision to buy the shop. He'd spoken of the nearness of the cinemas; he'd said that if he'd been younger, he'd have bought the shop himself and put a manager in; and as she was leaving he'd clasped her hand in his and said, "You're doing the right thing my dear, I'm sure of it." But as she walked through the town on her way home, her mind was a hazzmazz of difficulties. She'd got to sell her own business to start with and how was she going to alter the new premises. She'd have to have a new chip frying machine and a new counter. The whole place would need changing and what were the living quarters like? These and a thousand more questions filled her mind at the thought of what she'd got herself into. It was quite unlike her to act in such a way. It was the only time in her life she'd ever made such a decision. Every other move had been forced on her by circumstances but this time she'd jumped in head first and was very frightened about the consequences of such a rash action and yet, at the same time, she was excited at the prospects before her. She had now such a liking for money that the thought of all those hundreds of people coming out of the picture places each night into the chip shop caused her to shiver at the prospects. Mr Tongue had spoken to her as a business woman and it pleased her to think she was. When she looked back at her life, everything that had happened to her seemed inevitable. She realised that she was in a small way a woman of substance, different from her sisters, who were now no more than drudges.

She'd always known one clear thing. That was she didn't want a life like her mother's or her sisters' or for that matter any of the women in the streets round about. She'd seen enough blarting babies and drunken husbands; she shuddered at the thought. Meeting Mrs. Ginders had been the best thing that had happened to her. There was only one way out of the streets she'd been reared in, and that was money. It was better than any husband; it didn't drink or hit you and if you put it in the bank it grew and grew. You always knew where your were with money; you never did with people. There wasn't a single person she really trusted. Her sisters had no more sense now than when they were little children. When they were around her with their babies squawking and blarting, she was thankful her life was different from theirs. She felt proud of what she'd achieved. It meant nothing to her that Ada, the sister younger than her, had called her a skinny bugger. They were all jealous of her. A business woman, that's what she was, like Mr. Tongue had said and when she thought of the new shop she knew she'd done the right thing, even though she was filled with worries about it.

The next few weeks were fraught with anxiety. It was selling her own shop that caused her most worry. Then one day Mr. Tongue who was dealing with both the selling and the buying end of the deal told her that his solicitors had decided to buy her old shop for two hundred pounds. Hearing this was as though a great weight had been lifted from her shoulders. She knew then there was no turning back. She'd burnt her boats and was glad of it; she'd be right in the middle of things in Waterloo Road, right in the heart of the town. It would be work from morning till late at night but she wasn't afraid of that. Oh no, she just wanted to get at it and hear that till singing — the sweetest music she'd ever heard.

Only one thing troubled her; her bronchitis was getting worse. Some mornings when she got up, her chest was sore and rattled with phlegm, and often she felt suddenly flushed and weak. My father Len who was out of work was helping in the shop, fetching and carrying, attending to the fires and doing a lot of the heavy work and it soon got around the streets that the old shop was changing hands. Cissie was angry at this as the only people she'd told were Len and Lily and they both denied telling anybody. but Cissie knew she'd made a mistake in telling Len as he'd never been able to keep anything to himself.

The actual signing of the contract to buy the new shop came as luck would have it on her thirty third birthday. This pleased her as she said three had always been her lucky number, though Lily reckoned before this she'd always said it was number seven. Anyway when she went into the solicitors to sign on her birthday, she felt that all the signs were right and when she told Mr Tongue it was her birthday, he made a great fuss about it and offered her a drink of sherry which made her feel quite tipsy. After she'd signed and was about to leave, there was a noise in the passage. A moment later the door was opened by a young woman trying to manoeuvre an invalid chair in which sat a fat old man who Cissie recognised as Lanky Fred Potts. He must now have been in his eighties and was obviously quite helpless.

Mr Tongue at once shouted at him as though he was deaf. "Ah Mr. Potts, I'm glad you've come now. This is the young woman who's buying your premises."

The old man in the chair looked at Cissie and slowly shook his head. "You'll have good luck and bad, same as me I reckon;

still that's the same everywhere. You conna back a winner everyday; nobody can." His voice was slurred as he said this.

Mr Tongue then bent down closer to his face. "She's a Miss Salt, Miss Cissie Salt," he shouted. The old man looked at her again.

"Salt!" he repeated and a faint smile came across his features. " I've known her years mate, and I knew her fayther before her. Saml Salt wont it duck? He used to be up and down with a horse and cart years ago."

"You once called me a pinch of salt," Cissie said. But it didn't seem to register with him as his tongue came through his lips and he began to cough and splutter.

At once the woman with him undid his shirt collar. "He's got asthma," she said. He was nearly choking and his face was coloured like uncooked pastry with two pink blotches on his cheeks. Cissie and Mr. Tongue stood helpless as the woman did her best to help him. The attack went on for a few minutes and then he began to breathe easier and stopped coughing.

Mr Tongue muttered, "Thank God for that. I should get him home dear, he's in no state to be out. He should be in bed."

As the old man heard this, he looked across at Cissie and gasped, "It's better than the churchyard but not much." His mouth fell open and spit ran from his bottom lip. The woman he was with turned his invalid chair toward the door and as she was pushing it out he turned toward Cissie and Mr. Tongue and said something which neither of them could properly hear.

Mr. Tongue bent toward him and shouted: "You get yourself off home. I'll come to see you there, go to bed and rest."

A faint smile came across the old man's face as he heard this, "Bed, ah! There's nowt gotten in bed but children." Then his gaze focussed on Cissie and as he attempted to wipe the spit from his lower lip, he said in a voice that sounded as though he'd got something stuck in his throat, "There's nowt in old age duck!"

The woman pushing him turned his chair into the passage and a moment later he was gone. Mr. Tongue gave a great sigh of relief. "Oh dear, for a moment I thought we were about to have a death on our hands. He's a remarkable old man. They don't make them like that any more. Now Cissie I'm just off for lunch so I'll walk down past the Town Hall with you. It's been a memorable morning for you my dear," he said putting on his hat and coat.

As they walked down Price Street he began to speak of the way the town was changing and how the internal combustion engine had completely altered life. Cissie who had no idea of what an internal combustion engine was, hurried along beside him saying nothing. When they came to end of the street, by the District Bank, he clasped her hand and looked intently at her. "Don't worry. You're doing the right thing, Cissie. I'm sure of it. You have to speculate to accumulate; always remember that my dear."

"Speculate to accumulate." After he'd said that he touched his trilby hat, said good morning and made his way across the road to the Conservative Club. Cissie stood for a moment thinking about what he'd said. She'd never heard the phrase "speculate to accumulate" before. It struck her as very true and she kept repeating it to herself as she made her way toward the centre of the town for fear she would forget it and she resolved to write it down on a piece of paper when she got home. Speculate to accumulate, that's what she'd do. Without knowing it, she'd speculated. She hadn't realised that such big important sounding words applied to her but they did and it pleased her. She thought of her sisters and their husbands. She'd tell 'em "You've got to speculate to accumulate."

As neither of them had got two halfpennies for a penny and never would have, this caused her to smile to herself. As she crossed the road her attention was suddenly drawn by the sight of a crane lowering what looked like a big iron bar over the public lavatories which had been shut for repairs. She had never seen such a big crane before and it reminded her of when she'd gone with Lily on a day trip one Sunday to Blackpool and one of the children had put a penny in a machine where a little crane grasped and attempted to lift presents of one kind or another up. But it always seemed to drop them and as she stared at the big iron bar hanging in the air she shuddered at the thought of it dropping on her head. She hurried away but as she tried to remember the saying she'd kept repeating to herself, she found she'd forgotten it and no matter how hard she tried she just couldn't call it back. She knew it applied to her. Oh she'd got a memory like a sieve. There were so many things on her mind, so many things to do. She wondered how she was going to do them all.

That night she could hardly sleep for thinking about them and began to wish she'd never started the whole business. But she resolved to ask Mr. Tongue to write the saying down on a piece of paper for her if only she could remember enough of it to tell him what the saying was.

The next three months were so filled with upheaval that I will only attempt to give some blurred account of them. Cissie was ill most of the time as everything seemed covered in dust which affected her chest. She was coughing on and off from morning till night and often it was worse in the night. She tried everything to get some relief but nothing worked for long and for the first time she came to appreciate the help she got from sister in law Lily and her brother Len, for both worked like Trojans on her behalf. Sometimes it seemed that they might have been working for themselves, and as she had no family of her own it struck her during one of her bad coughing bouts, that they might be, if anything happened to her. Len, being her nearest relative could expect to inherit her money. The thought of this caused her some dismay as she couldn't bear to think of anybody touching what was hers, but she never mentioned this or anything about such matters to him. The thought of dying never entered her mind, but Len and Lily worked as hard as she did in the shop and when Lanky Fred finally vacated his cafe it was Len who got stuck into the thousands of jobs that needed doing.

The first and major one was the installation of a new chip fryer with three pans. Cissie who had remembered the phrase "You've got to speculate to accumulate", had taken it to heart and from a catalogue of the local builders merchants had chosen a magnificent yellow and black tiled chip fryer which had cost her nearly as much as the shop premises. Len had prepared the back wall of the shop to receive it, but when it arrived it was too big, and there were panic stations. but somehow, he found a way of overcoming the difficulty. Then Cissie who had intended to bring the counter from her old shop decided to have a new one and Len got a mate of his, an out of work joiner, to make one and fit it for at least half the price it would have cost anybody else. It seemed that when any problem arose, Len always knew somebody who would do the job cheap. The district was filled with unemployed men and it was cheap labour that helped get Cissie installed in the new shop, as men would do a days work for the price of a couple of pints and packet of woodbines.

The living quarters of the new shop were no better than the ones in Stringer Street. In fact the ceiling in the upstairs bedroom was lower and the stairs were steeper and there was the continual noise of traffic passing them from the early hours of the morning till well after midnight. But Cissie shut all these difficulties from her mind and thought about the takings.

The new chip fryer was much admired by all who saw it. There wasn't another like it in the district, but as usual there were certain teething troubles. When she tried to light the fire in the fire box, the shop filled with smoke which set her coughing so bad she had to go outside for fresh air. When Len examined it he couldn't understand why it was blocked up as the flue was clear. Then he discovered that the chimney on top of the shop was partly blocked by something. He climbed on the roof and found a number of dead birds stuck on top of a protruding brick end. When he managed to clear this, the fire worked perfectly and Cissie soon got the hang of lighting it.

During this time she had shut up the old shop but was still sleeping there. The last day of September was a day of wind and rain, a day that she remembered all her life. She stood with Lily while Len unscrewed the old iron chip machine her father had first installed years ago. Then she went into every room to have a last look. She saw the back door was locked, and after Len and Lily had gone outside, she had one further look, then pulled the front door shut with a bang and made her way toward the Waterloo Road and the next phase of her life.

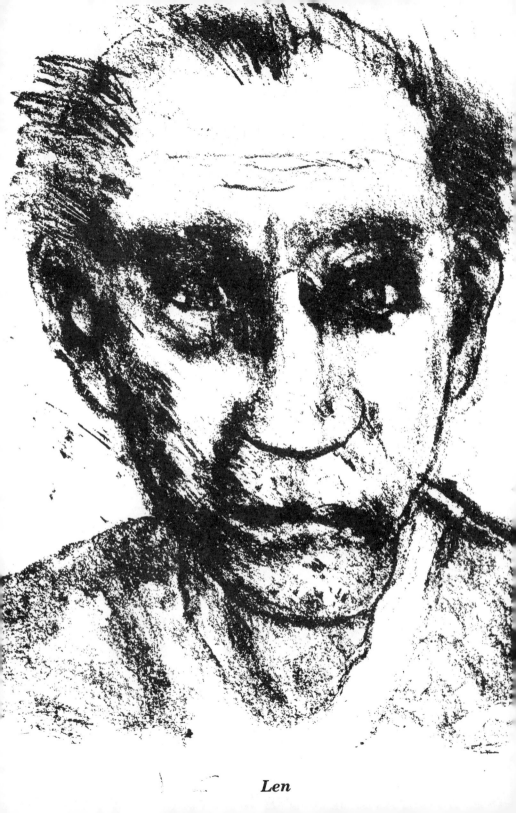

Len

Chapter Four

I remember the day the new shop opened because George Raft was on in a picture called "Bolero" at the Palladium which was directly opposite the shop. The film stuck in my mind because of the theme music. It was the first time I had ever heard a piece of music that really thrilled me, and as I emerged from the dark picture palace in the Waterloo Road my mind was throbbing with the lush richness and dramatic beat of it. But no sooner was I out of the building and standing on the pavement than I was shocked by the sight of my father standing in the front door of the shop with a white apron on, and my Auntie Cissie just behind him. After seeing the film and hearing such music, it made me realise how limited and miserable life was in the town I lived in and how different it must be in other places.

I was at that time much filled with daydreams and was greatly addicted to the pictures, often going if I could raise the few pence entrance money, three or even four times a week. The illusionary world I found in the darkness of the picture palaces was much more to my liking than the world of the streets I lived in. So all this fuss my parents were making about Aunty Cissie's new shop meant little or nothing to me and it was only when I saw the sign "Cissie Salt, Fish and Chips" my father had laboriously painted in our back kitchen that I felt the shop had anything to do with me or our family.

I'd never had much to do with Aunty Cissie as she didn't like kids, and it had only been since my father came out of the pit and started doing odd jobs for her that I'd ever thought much about her. We weren't a close family. I'd even got a lot of cousins I couldn't recognise if I passed them in the street, but in the last month or two it had been our Cissie this, our Cissie that, every day in our house. My sister Phoebe had turned on my father and called Aunty Cissie 'a scrawming old hag', and a row followed. But then Phoebe and my father were always at it, about her coming in late and being up and down with lads. He said she took after Uncle Charlie who was no good and never had been and if her didn't alter her'd come to a bad end. I wouldn't write down here what Phoebe said to him under her breath but I heard it, and it was a good job he didn't as he'd a killed her.

She seemed to like to torment him. She'd stand in front of the mirror putting face powder and lipstick on although she was only just fourteen and this would always make him mad. Many times he threatened what he'd do to her; but Phoebe was frightened of nothing and my father knew it. My mother tried to

stop them falling out but it was no use. If they were in the same
room together for five minutes you could guarantee there'd be a
row. I had helped when they were getting the shop ready, and my
Aunty Cissie promised to let me have her free tickets for the
picture palaces as they were going to give 'em her for putting
their posters up in her shop window. This was perfect for me but
Phoebe wouldn't help. She said she didn't want to stink of fish
and chips and she could get blokes to take her to the pictures.

The day before the new shop opened there was great
excitement in our house. My father said he hadn't slept a wink
and was up just after four o'clock in the morning. My mother was
all of a twitter, and all three of them, my father, mother, and
Aunty Cissie were wearing new white aprons when they opened
the front door for the first time.

The first customer was a woman, name of Annie Tuffnell.
She'd come up specially from Stringer Street and had been a
regular customer at the old chip shop. She made a great fuss of
being the first in the new shop.

"I'll be there the minute that door opens Cissie," she'd
regularly announced for months before, and was decked up in her
best clothes when at last she stepped in the shop. On seeing the
new gleaming chip machine, she shrieked aloud "Oh duck, it's
beautiful, oooh! I've been in some chip shops in my life, but I've
never seen one like that. My God Cissie, I'll bet that's set you
back a pretty penny".

"That's just a free sample duck," Aunty Cissie joked.

Then Mr Tongue appeared. "I've come to see the ship
launched. Have you got the champagne?" he said, taking his
trilby off and flourishing it like royalty. "My word, everything
looks shipshape and gleaming." Aunty Cissie at once offered to
serve him a chip to sample, but he refused it and had a look into
the back room where my mother was standing. Cissie introduced
them.

With another flourish, he said, "This I prophesy will be a
great success Miss Cissie Salt. You're a very lucky young woman,
I'm convinced of it. You're on a winner here my dear. Remember
what I said, 'You've got to speculate to accumulate', that's always
been my motto."

As he said this, a horse passing the shop pulling a wagon
loaded with coal bags made a noise that horses make, neither a
neigh, nor a cough, more a snort, then a blubbering of the lips.

On hearing this, Mr. Tongue smiled and nodded. "There,
what did I tell you, the horse agrees with me." This caused much
laughing and Annie Tufnell began to tell how long she'd known

Cissie and how she'd been a regular customer at the old shop and what marvellous chips Cissie fried.

"I've never tasted nicer, duck and although I say it meself and her's here to hear it, I can honestly say I've never tasted nicer chips and I should know. I've had 'em most days in me life. My husband always says he'd rather have chips than a Christmas dinner. I've reared my family on 'em."

Cissie well knew that once Annie started she could go on in this fashion for ages; once in full flow, there was no stopping her. Mr. Tongue must have realised this too, for replacing his hat on his head he cut in, "Well I must love you and leave you. I've got a lot of soliciting to do this afternoon but I shall call again, have no fear my dear. We've got our eye on you up at the office."

He stepped out on the pavement and they thought he was about to go. Instead he stood for a moment staring up Waterloo Road, then turning and stepping back into the shop he said, "You know, I was reared in Card Street and spent my boyhood in this road. I clearly remember walking in the procession with Hill Top Sunday School at Easter time. I can see my dear father now, carrying a banner and I can also see myself as a young child with an iron bowler and a hoop." He smiled as he said this. "A child couldn't do that now with all this traffic. Oh times do change don't they, it's all films now. They tell me how marvellous these talking pictures are. I haven't seen them myself and don't intend to. I've no appetite for that sort of thing." He looked sad as he said this, then lifted his forefinger as though he'd identified something in his mind. "This shop will be a little gold-mine, mark my words, Cissie. The picture palaces will make you a fortune; I'm convinced of it." Then he touched his hat and was gone.

"My word Cissie, did you hear that, 'a little gold-mine'. Who's that gentleman?" Annie Tuffnell asked.

"Oh he's a solicitor," Cissie answered, irritated that Annie had heard the remark.

"He's only a solicitors clerk if the truth be known," my father interrupted.

Cissie, turned on him angrily. "Well solicitor or solicitor's clerk, he's a gentleman, Mr. Tongue is. He's been unknown good ter me."

"Oh he's a gentleman all right, you can see that. There aren't many round here," Annie Tuffnell cut in.

"Not like him there." Aunt Cissie added sharply, angry that Mr. Tongue had made the remark about the shop being a gold mine when other people were present. It was something she'd wanted to keep to herself. Knowing my mother Lily and my father Len and particularly Annie Tuffnell, she realised that it was just the sort of saying they'd go on repeating.

In the next few months, Mr. Tongue's remark proved to be true. Cissie had expected she'd have to build up trade but the shop took off at once. The very first day there was a queue outside, and when the picture palaces closed, she was run off her feet. My father and I served behind the counter while she attended to the till, a job she'd allow no one else to do. Then when the many pubs in the town shut, the shop was full again. It was the same every night and at weekends. We couldn't serve fast enough. She was taking more in one night than she'd taken in a week at the old shop. Every night as she counted the takings her hands would tremble. She'd never seen so much money in her life and soon began to be afraid of the shop being burgled, so she started to deposit the takings in the night safe of Lloyds Bank. My father and mother acted as her bodyguards and escorted her there, my father carrying a thick walking stick for protection.

This sudden increase in her earning made her more money conscious than ever. She'd always been a great adder up of coppers; now she was counting half crowns and it soon became an obsession. She became meaner about any expenditure and quibbled over a few pence. When my mother suggested that she gave people who brought old newspaper to the shop to use as wrapping paper a helping of chips for nothing, she was indignant and said it was her doing them a good turn by taking them not the other way around. Stories of her meanness began to spread. There were rumours that she kept boxes full of half crowns covered in chip fat beside her bed. Then one night a loutish youth ran out of the shop carrying his chips without paying.

When Cissie realised what had happened she screamed a terrible anguished scream and rushing from behind the counter, chased the youth shouting, "Stop thief, stop thief," all the way up Queen Street. She collapsed outside the institute building, and as a crowd gathered, she was still gasping "stop thief," with what breath she had left. This incident made her ill, though it was not collapsing in the street and being on the point of death but being robbed of the few pence for the chips that upset her.

For weeks after she called the Police Station every day to see if the thief had been caught. This love of money grew in her as the chip shop flourished and after a few months she was having interviews with the bank manager about investments. The shop was doing better than she'd ever imagined. But for all this she lived frugally and never spent a penny on herself or the living quarters. In fact she lived like a pauper. My mother used to wonder how she managed to exist and work on the little food she ate.

One day my father arrived at the shop to find the back door still locked. He got no answer and at once sensed that something was wrong. Then he heard groaning from inside so he broke a back kitchen window, got his arm through, undid the latch and managed to climb in to find Cissie lying at the bottom of the staircase in obvious pain. He tried to help her to her feet but she cried out and he had to stop. Then by turning her on her side and putting her weight on her right leg he lifted her into a sitting position with her groaning all the time.

She told him she'd fallen head first from the top to the bottom of the stairs. She'd heard the postman put some letters through the letterbox, and never having much mail, was so curious about what it might be that she'd got out of bed without putting anything on her feet and started to come down stairs. The skin on the bottom of her feet was shiny, particularly on her heels, and as she was too mean to put any stair carpet down, and had left the strips of shiny lino that were there when she'd taken possession, she'd slipped on one of these.

As she lay groaning she kept on and on about the pains at the bottom of her back, and my father thought he'd better ring for an ambulance. Making her as comfortable as he could, he hurried across to the Billiard Hall where there was a phone. In half an hour the ambulance came and although she begged him to stay and attend to the shop, he went with her to the accident unit at the Hospital.

"Whatever am I going ter do?" she kept moaning in the ambulance. "There'll be nobody there when the fish comes. Oh whatever am I going ter do."

The nurse in the ambulance tried to calm her down but it was no use. She was nearly demented with worry and pain and when they got her on a stretcher at the hospital, she made my father promise to go back to the shop at once and open as usual.

As they wheeled her inside she kept giving him a string of instructions. "Don't forget, write everything down on a piece of paper, how much you've taken every single penny piece and bring it to the hospital and don't let anybody else anywhere near that till. I'm trusting to you Leonard." She beseeched him to do all she said as she was fully expecting to have to spend some time in the hospital. When my father got back to the shop, he and my mother opened as usual at dinner time; then they prepared for the evening.

I was working for the Co-op at the time and promised to help serve in the shop. But our Phoebe refused. She was fifteen years of age and had only just left school but she was a big busted girl and could have easily been taken for years older. She'd got long lustrous hair and was much courted by various local youths, a fact which greatly pleased her. Every night she was the centre of a group of them who stood at the street corner. This infuriated my father and when he came home from the shop he would stand at our front door staring angrily at them, shouting "Phoebe, Phoebe" till she came reluctantly in. Some nights she'd go dancing. Those were the nights of the big rows, and often my father threatened to hit her. But when he did she'd stand and face him. "Go on then, hit me, go on, go on", she'd taunt him. But he never laid a finger on her. She knew he wouldn't for fear of what she might do, as she had threatened to leave home on a number of occasions. So when he asked her to help out in the chip shop, he expected the answer he always got.

"Why should I help her, what's her ever done for me? Bloody nothing, the skinny old bugger." And on the day of the accident she still refused to help out.

My mother tried to remonstrate with her but it was no use. I knew the real reason for her never helping in the shop. It was that people who worked in chip shops stank. All this, as it happened, proved not to be necessary, for at around six o'clock in the evening, as my father was busy behind the counter, a taxi drew up and out got Aunty Cissie with her leg bandaged up and a crutch. With the help of the taxi driver, she hobbled into the shop.

"Get me a chair," she said breathlessly. When she was sat down she counted some coins carefully and paid the taxi driver. "There's nothing broken, thank God. Me ankle's twisted and I've bruised me back. They wanted ter keep me in all night but I told 'em I was a business woman. The doctors face lit up. He thought he was getting a pound or two out of me, but he'd another think coming, and yer know, I heard one of the nurses say I was nothing but skin and bone. When I told her about it, her said her hadn't said it, the lying young bugger did. Yer know it's the first time I've been in a taxi and I don't want for go in one again. It cost me ten shillings and I was thankful for pay it. Oh Leonard, I was glad get out of that place. There was one man there in front of me as kept retching and choking. His face was purple and when I was lying there all me life went through me mind. I could see me father's pony and cart. I could see Mrs. Ginders as clear as I can see you standing there, all them as are dead and gone I could see, and I kept thinking as folks die in hospital and I must get out or I should be the next."

She went on and on for the best part of an hour in this fashion, then she became exhausted and slumped on a chair in the back kitchen. But when the first customers came into the shop, she shouted for my father to fix a chair with a cushion against the till and with much wincing, she sat propped there taking the money all night. For months her back was black and blue with bruises and she couldn't put any weight on her left leg, but there was no way she'd leave the till to anybody else.

This accident was the beginning of a run of bad luck. The chip fryer still smoked from time to time and she decided to have the chimney swept. But when the sweep pushed his brush up the flue, there was a terrible clatter from the roof and a number of building bricks fell past the front window. Fortunately nobody was passing at the time. What had happened was that the brush had hit a brick inside the chimney and as the mortar between the bricks was worn away, the whole top of the chimney had come down. A few weeks after this a drain got blocked in the backyard and had to be dug up. This was brought to her attention by the man who kept the shop next door, a Mr. Slack, who was known among the pigeon fanciers locally as Puffer Slack.

He sold dog biscuits and pigeon corn and all sorts of fishing equipment and was a man much concerned about territory. It was months before he spoke to Cissie after she'd taken the shop over and then it was to complain about the smell of fish. He was a man of about sixty, with a face that resembled a bird with a sore beak, and as he spoke he always seemed to be nibbling what looked like hen corn. He was well known as an authority on birds and bred budgerigars. He was also a judge at rabbit shows, and was so proud of this that he displayed a silver cup in his window along with a framed photograph of himself with a sash on, presenting a cup to the winner of the yearly rabbit show at the Town Hall.

Cissie couldn't abide the sight of him and just ignored his complaint, till one day as she was in the backyard with my father, she sniffed the air and smelt something rotten. At first she thought it was the fish but when they examined it she found it wasn't. After much sniffing around she couldn't find where the smell was coming from and as it was particularly foetid and seemed to be strongest somewhere near the grid, she came to the conclusion that it must be the drains. At first she did nothing about it hoping that it would go away, but it didn't and in fact it got worse. Reluctantly she decided to have the backyard dug up, and as usual my father knew a bloke as would do it cheap. So one morning Harry Toft turned up with a pick and spade.

Tofty, as he was called, was only about five feet high, had a sallow wrinkled complexion and looked generally rather monkeyfied. Cissie was dismayed when she first saw him for he didn't seem strong enough to lift a pick and shovel up, and as he spoke to her, he kept sniffing as though he'd got a blockage up his nose. My father assured her he was a good worker, so she left him to it and before dinner time he'd got half the yard up. Then he disappeared and didn't come back till late afternoon smelling strongly of drink.

Cissie at once set about him, "Where've yer been till now?"

He sat down on the ash bin and wiped his face with a piece of rag before he answered. "I went across the Jig Post for a pint and I met a mate of mine I hadn't seen for years." He stopped at this and looked down the hole. "I'll tell yer something Missus, there's nowt up with this drain. Yer know what that smell is. I could tell what it was as soon as I had a sniff. It's maggots."

"Maggots", Cissie repeated the word.

"Yes Missus, maggots from the shop next door. I've bought 'em myself off him."

Cissie stood dumbfounded, then when the full realisation of it dawned on her, her face flushed with anger. "I'll give him maggots when I see him."

"He keeps 'em in a tank down the yard in the fishing season. There's nowt as smells like maggots. I could tell as soon as I got here. It's all them bluebottles as does it; there's thousands there," Tofty said.

"Well why didn't yer say instead of digging the yard up?" Cissie scorped.

"I couldna be sure could I. It coulda been a dead rat stuck." As he said this, he pulled a little snuff box out of his waistcoat pocket and put a pinch on the back of his hand and sniffed it up. Then he offered the box to Cissie.

"No thank you," she said with a grimace.

"Have a pinch." He offered the box again. "I used to use it in the pit. I couldna do without it now. It's good stuff this is."

Cissie was about to refuse the snuff again, but for some strange reason she decided to try it and took a pinch. From that day on for the rest of her life she took snuff surreptitiously. My father and mother knew about it but nobody else did. My mother thought it was a filthy habit but kept her opinions to herself except when Cissie hadn't wiped the snuff off her nose. Then she'd tell her about it.

This often caused a little flash of impatience from Cissie, who'd snap back at her, "Lily, I don't drink. I don't go on holidays.

I don't got to the pictures. I don't spend money on clothes, so I think I'm entitled to a little pleasure now and again don't you? And any road it's nothing to do with you or anybody else what I do hasn't."

The business of the maggots was the beginning of a battle with Mr. Slack next door over what smell was what. He said it was the fish that was causing the stink. She said it was his maggots and there was row after row. One day Cissie threatened to chuck a bucket of water over him. He said he'd fetch the Police, and she told him to get on with it. This rowing went on for years and became a feature of their lives. Sometimes there would be a lull and they'd merely glare at one another over the wall. Then it would flare up again with threat and counter threat.

One day he didn't open his shop as usual and it was closed the next day as well. A customer in the chip shop said Mr. Slack had died suddenly of silent pneumonia. He'd been taken bad on Friday night and had thought nothing of it. But by Saturday he was much worse and they'd had to fetch the doctor in who'd sent for an ambulance to take him into hospital. But on Sunday morning he'd died. So the maggot war was over.

Cissie was very shocked at this and felt guilty. But the man who kept the builders shop at the corner told her, that, in his opinion Mr. Slack had died of drink as he'd been drinking a bottle of Whisky a day for years. This somehow relieved her guilty feelings as she was by now very bigoted against drink. A few weeks later, Mr. Slack's shop was sold to a man named Aaron Wootten, a little fat necked unshaven man who wore a trilby with the brim turned up all round and was so short sighted he had to press his face close to you as he talked. He also tended to spit on you a bit as he pronounced certain words but he became a good customer of the chip shop. Indeed, he seemed to live on little else and soon became a gossiping friend of Cissie's.

When first he took the shop over he carried it on as a pet shop, but after a few weeks began to extend into other lines. Soon his shop window was packed with all sorts of miscellaneous objects — pink combs, syrup of figs, Indian brandy, oil lamps, pegs, scrubbing brushes, paper bags filled with coal, rubber stick-on soles, tins of shoe blacking, bars of carbolic soap, washing powder, fly paper, candles, and a notice saying he also sold paraffin which he kept in the same metal container that Puffer Slack had kept his maggots in; and outside, hanging on a nail, jutting out over the pavement, he hung a zinc bathtub. When this was delivered, he made Cissie laugh by sitting in it, pretending to bath himself. His wife Florrie who lived upstairs with three young children often came into the chip shop. She was a scrawny looking yellow faced woman who could often be heard through the wall screeching at one or other of her children, or at Aaron.

Not long after he'd taken the shop over, Cissie heard Aaron shouting at somebody, "Gerr off, I've told you yer a bloody pest. I don't want nothing do with you. Yer bone stinking idle; there's nothing here for yer; yer no brother of mine."

The kids started blarting and she heard Florrie scream. "Get gone. Sod off and don't come here no more." Then a door slammed

The next day Aaron told her it was his brother Cocky Wootten, who'd come to visit them.

"I told him he's no brother er mine. He's been in five different jails. He's got a houseful of kids. It was him as killed me mother. He'll pinch anything. He pinched money out 'er me mother's purse when her lay dying. Oooh, I tell you. He's a whoostercaster, our Cocky is. He's no brother er mine! They say blood's thicker than water. I say there's a lot er things thicker than water. He isn't married ter that woman he lives with, and they've got five kids! One of the poor little buggers fell out of the bedroom winder and him and her lay stinking in bed. They had ter give 'em a Council house and the silly bugger got a big hammer and knocked one of the inside walls down and the ceiling fell in. He said he was sick of walking in and out of the back kitchen. What can yer do with a man like that? He once tried to join the Foreign Legion. They are supposed ter have the scum of the earth, but they wouldn't have Cocky! Then he joined up Oswald Mosley's lot, but it was only because they gave him a free black shirt. He's after anything for nothing. He's no brother er mine!"

It amused Cissie to listen to his troubles, and when he used to stand at his front door at night and watch the queues outside the chip shop, he'd say "Oh Cissie you must be rolling in it."

Usually any kind of remark about what money she was making would make her angry. Certainly if either my mother or father mentioned anything about the takings she'd shut them up by saying it had nothing to do with them. But Aaron and his continual predicaments amused her so much that she'd stand it.

"Oh I don't know Aaron, I've got a lot 'er debt," or "Don't you know I've a job make ends meet," she'd banter. A genuine feeling of friendship grew between them, but this didn't extend to any cut price helpings of fish and chips although Aaron often called in at closing time and asked about what they did with anything they'd got left over.

Chapter Five

As far as I can calculate, this would be in the middle of the nineteen thirties and the name of Hitler was beginning to appear in the newspapers. I had finished at the Co-op, had a job at a colour works and was courting a girl called Mavis. She was a big girl, and very passionate in her embraces — more passionate than I was, and often when I arranged to meet her, I'd wish that I hadn't, as I'd begun to realise that I'd much rather have two or three pints of beer in the bar of some pub, than stand in some dark entry necking and feeling Mavis.

Our Phoebe was in a lot of trouble at that time. Her'd got a friend called Ivy Birtles, and folks spread it about as Ivy'd had a baby and drowned it in the marlhole. The bobbies had her and our Phoebe in the police station questioning 'em about it and somebody must a come in the chip shop and told me Aunty Cissie it was our Phoebe; and when Cissie told me father there was hell up in our house. My father called her a dirty bitch and Phoebe went to pack her bags. My mother tried for stop her, and my father said as her'd got stop mating out with Ivy Birtles as her was the same as her mother, a prostitute. Then Phoebe said how did he know her was a prostitute; perhaps he'd been with her. This started my mother who smacked her in the face. Then Phoebe went to throw a glass vase off the mantlepiece at my father, but he managed to grab her hand before her could let it go. But her did manage ter catch him in the eye with it as they were struggling, and for days he had a big black eye. It ended with him telling her to get herself fresh lodgings. Phoebe was then working on a pot bank and was supposed ter be courting a fellow called Syd Clithery, who had a business selling sack bags. He was supposed ter have plenty of money but a bloke who worked on our place and lived next door to him just laughed when I told him.

"Slithery Clithery got plenty er money? He's got nothing. He's drawing dole. Business inna his. He just does an odd day driving for the bloke as owns it."

When I told Phoebe this, she just laughed and said she'd chucked him up and was leaving the pot bank as she'd got a job as an usherette in the Colosseum. There was nothing unusual in this as Phoebe was always chucking blokes up and often had two or three hanging round after her. There was hardly a night when her wasn't down the entry with some fella till nearly midnight. But my father was at the chip shop till well after that. He didna know what time her came in.

My Aunty Cissie was now beginning to suffer with arthritis and had a lot of back pain. She reckoned it had all started from when she fell down stairs. My father told her that she should take things a bit easier; perhaps have a holiday or even from time to time have a drink. This last advice was more to her liking and she began to have a drop of sherry at night, and sometimes more than a drop.

One Sunday, my mother and father took her to a fete in the park. These fetes were held every year and when they arrived the park was full. Hundreds of people were sitting on the grass in their summer clothes and there were a number of marquees and side shows, but unfortunately the park lake was empty as a crack had opened in the bottom due to pit subsidence and all the water had drained away.

The park was on a slope and there were steps leading from one tier to the next while at the top there were tennis courts and bowling greens. In the centre stood a black and white building, which at weekends in summer sold ice cream. Rhododendron bushes and flower beds were dotted around. Cissie and my parents much admired them. Then they went toward the bandstand where the Co-operative Band was giving a concert and as Cissie had begun to complain about her back, they found three seats against a terra-cotta balustrade. The bandsmen were resting, and a number of them were sitting on seats nearby having a smoke. A small boy about five years of age ran past with a bandsman's hat. As he passed my Aunty Cissie, the hat being a lot too big for him, fell off and rolled under the wooden seat. A moment later a bandsman came running after the child.

"Come here yer little monkey," he said affectionately to the boy. Then when he saw where his hat was he said, "Excuse me Madam, I'll get my hat if you don't mind."

Cissie got up and the bandsman went on his knees as the hat had rolled at the back of the seat. When he'd retrieved it, he stood up and dusted the knees of the trousers of his blue uniform. He put the hat on the little lad again, said "sorry to have troubled you," and walked off toward the bandstand.

Cissie staring after him said. "He seems a nice man doesn't he? I wonder if the little lad's his. He looks a bit old ter be the father."

"Perhaps he's the Grandad," my father said.

Cissie nodded thoughtfully at this. Little did any of them realise that meeting that bandsman was to prove a significant event in their lives. They were involved in another unusual event. My Aunty Cissie bought all of them an ice cream, but

Phoebe

unfortunately they strolled into the bird aviary as they were eating them and the smell of the birds caused Cissie to start sneezing to such an extent that she dropped her cream cone. She was upset at this and said she'd seen enough and wanted to go home so they made their way out of the park.

As they got to the main road they saw Harry Toft coming out of a public house. Cissie was for hurrying on, but as soon as Tofty saw them he shouted across the road. He was making his way towards them when a car nearly ran him down. He shook his fist and swore at the driver who swore back as he drove on.

"Did you see that bloody idiot?" he spluttered. Obviously the worse for drink, he swayed as he stood in front of them, his bleary eyes fixed on Cissie.

"I could smell maggots soon as I stepped in your yard. I've never seen bluebottles like 'em. How yer going on missus. How's the world using yer?"

"Oh very well thank you Mr. Toft," Cissie said, edging away from him.

"You've just been up the park have yer. It's years since I was in there. They tell me the pool's emptied; and how are you Len and Missus Len?"

He felt in his waistcoat pocket, pulled his snuffbox out and carefully opening it was about to take a pinch when instead he offered it to Cissie. "Here have a pinch an this duck. I know yer partial to it."

Cissie at once recoiled.

"Oh no thank you Mr. Toft. I hardly ever use it these days."

He took a pinch himself then carefully put the box back in his pocket. "He went very sudden, Puffer Slack did, didna he? They tell me he was right as ninepence one minute and the next he was in his box." He looked very thoughtful after he said this, as though the fragility of existence had struck through the fug of drink and sobered him. Then he looked helplessly at them and stuck his hand out for them to shake.

My father took it. "We are all in the same boat Harry, yer know what they say; 'keep dipping your bread'."

At this Aunty Cissie and my mother pulled away, "Come on Len, we've got a lot of work to do."

"Good afternoon Mr. Toft,' Cissie said.

Tofty held his hand out for her to shake but she ignored it and he stood staring at her slightly bemused. Then his face lit up as though he had just remembered something.

"As soon as I stepped in your yard I could smell 'em. There's nowt as smells like maggots." At this he made a gesture of saluting them. "Ta ra duck, look after yourself. There inner many of us old 'uns left." He turned and made his way up the road.

Cissie's face was white with anger. "Old uns!" she said, "I'll give him old uns. How old does he think I am? He must be old enough to be my father!"

"Take no notice," my father said. "He's three parts drunk. He dunna know what he's saying half the time even when he's sober, Tofty dunna."

"Oh I don't know so much. He must a thought it else he wouldn't er said it," Cissie snapped angrily. She was not a vain woman and never had taken much care of her appearance, but lately when she'd caught sight of her reflection at the centre of the chip machine, she'd been shocked by what she'd seen. Recently she'd been troubled by bleeding gums, and had some side teeth pulled out, so her cheeks had sunk in. This had made her chin seem to be more prominent. Also her hair was now streaked with grey and after a full day behind the counter sweating against the chip fryer she looked like an old woman, and worse still — a fierce old woman. As she stood in the road white faced with the shock and anger of what Harry Toft had just said, she realised that what had upset her was that it was true. She did look much older than her age, which was now somewhere in the middle forties. Certainly she was nowhere near as old as Harry Toft.

This sad little happening took root in her mind and for weeks after, whenever she passed the mirror she'd glance at herself, and for the first time in her life she began to put a dab of face powder on and resolved to buy herself a few new clothes.

One day as she was passing the meat market, she saw a man in a busman's uniform drawing some letters with coloured chalks on a black board. She stopped to watch him as sometimes she herself had to write notices with chalk and put them in her shop window, but she now realised that she was nowhere near as skilful as the man she was watching. He did all capital letters in red then put thick blue lines round them and added some white chalk marks as well to set the letters off. The result was very impressive.

"Blackpool illuminations six shillings return, Sunday September 14th," it said. There were a number of these notices in front of a booking office in the portico of the black stone meat market and she thought how attractive they looked. Later in the day the thought of Blackpool illuminations kept coming into her mind. She couldn't imagine what they'd look like. She'd heard people go on about how marvellous they were, but she'd never really thought about them seriously.

She'd been to Blackpool twice when she was a child, and remembered how crowded the sands were, and how she'd been afraid of getting lost amongst all the people, and she clearly recalled standing in the sea and watching her naked toes press into the sand. She also remembered the journey back in the bus when the men were drinking bottled beer, and how the bus had to keep stopping while they got out to have a pee. She'd not been to Blackpool or seen the sea for nearly forty years and a sudden excited longing to see the illuminations came over her. But even as it did she realised that she wouldn't like to go alone.

Although an independent woman, she couldn't be on her own for very long without needing somebody to talk to. At the same time she was calculating the cost. She knew my mother wouldn't go without my father, so that meant she'd have to pay for three tickets, that is if they wanted to go at all. She was used to have both do as she wanted, and when she put it to them that she'd pay the fare, they readily agreed.

My mother read in some paper that George Formby was switching the lights on, and as he was a great favourite of my Aunty Cissie she was quite excited at the prospect of seeing him. Then it was explained to her that he didn't switch them on every night, and the coach trip was more than a fortnight after the opening. She enquired at the booking office if they'd a trip on the opening night. They had, but said it was booked up, at which she was most disappointed.

Her liking for George Formby was fed by her window cleaner, a man named Tommy Frizzell, who was also a great fan of the comedian and could imitate him. Every time he came to clean the shop window, he'd give Cissie a rendering of one of George's songs. This amused her greatly and Tommy became one of the people she was genuinely fond of. He was a well creased man of fifty with skin like a washleather, who never wore anything but his crumpled overalls and a cap which always looked soaking wet. I knew him through regularly meeting him in the pubs where he was a well known character who couldn't pass a card game without wanting to join in. He was also a great gambler in horse racing and his talk was mostly about some horse or another that been beaten by a short head. He was skilled at reckoning bets up and for this was much sought after in tap rooms. He had many other sides to his personality as well, and I found him a most surprising fount of enthusiastic opinions about subjects you'd never expect he'd know anything about. Classical music was one of them. His overall pockets were stuffed with little scraps of news print he'd ripped out of some magazine or newspaper about the lives of great composers. Wagner was one of his heroes. He showed me a newspaper article with a photo of Wagner's house on Lake Lucerne and tried to sing a very dramatic passage from one of Wagner's operas in the bar of the Black Lion. This caused the other customers to look at him as though he was mad, but that didn't trouble him. Whenever he saw me he'd be filled with a tale about some great writer he'd read about. Sometimes it came out in a confused stream, where Harry Wragg, Gordon Richards or the Aga Khan would get mixed up with Rossini, Mozart or Bill Sykes. I do believe, that looking back, it was Tommy Frizzell who first got me to feel that there was another world outside chips shops and public houses. He certainly knew there was.

The lives of film stars were another of his interests. He could tell you who was married to who and whom they'd been married to before, where they lived, and what their real names were. He was also fascinated by ocean liners and knew which ports they were due to dock at and what their sailing dates were. Whenever he sang, the song was "Home in Pasadena where the grass is greener." He made it sound like a paradise far away from the mean streets of this town. As a child he'd been reared a Roman Catholic and had served as an altar boy. But as he'd grown older he'd fallen away from the church. When his mother was dying of cancer and the priest Father Cooney said she was in Paradise, Tommy had said she was in bloody agony. He told me he'd been excommunicated for this by the bell, book and candlelight, but I didn't believe him as he always made things either more dramatic or dafter than they really were.

He lived in a lodging house down by the canal, a tall dark bricked house where the back door was never closed. This was kept by a man named Hopwell, known as Hoppo, who was also a great authority on horse racing. A number of men lodged there, most of them on the edge of poverty and all of them with a great liking for drink. One thin faced shivering man called Snav always seemed to have a wet fag end hanging from his bottom lip. He had once played for Bolton Wanderers and when he was drunk, he'd open his shirt in whatever pub he happened to be drinking in to reveal that he was wearing an old Bolton Wanderers shirt for a vest. He would often get so drunk, he'd lie down on the pavement to sleep. Once I found him lying flat out on his back in front of the lodging house with a trail of pee running from his trousers across the pavement. Tommy Frizzell had lived there for years and called it Bleak House. Once I was passing and saw that someone had chalked "Balmoral" across the front door.

Most of the lodgers were customers of my Aunty Cissie's chip shop. A little sparky man they called Fitz sometimes stripped off in the queue, showing everybody his little muscles and challenging anyone who dared, to fight. One night a woman called Ethel Lally known locally as The Spade Ace took little Fitz's challenge up and with one smack with the flat of her hand knocked him down, much to the amusement of the rest of the queue, who shouted encouragement for him to get up and fight like a man. The blow Ethel had struck had somehow brought out belated feelings of gallantry from poor Fitz, who, as he staggered to his feet and saw Ethel taking up a fighting stance again, declared that he would never fight a woman. Some of the members of the queue shouted that he was yellow, but this made no difference to Fitz who'd had all the fight knocked out of him by one hefty smack. When he inveigled himself back in the queue he was very subdued and tried to pretend he was a gentleman and he'd let her hit him.

Incidents of this kind were fairly frequent in the queue and occasionally the Police were called, but Cissie knew the world she was in and it knew her, and such incidents didn't trouble her. The shop was now something of an institution in the town and by local standards she was a wealthy woman; one of the most valued customers of Lloyds Bank.

Nonetheless she was both pleased and surprised when she went to book the tickets for the day trip to the illuminations. The man who took her money and was writing the tickets out must have recognised her name for he looked up and said, "Not *the* Cissie Salt?"

"What d'yer mean?" she said looking perplexed.

"The famous Cissie Salt, the owner of Sissymints."

"'Sissymints?" she repeated the name as she'd never heard it before.

"Sissymints, the chip shop," the man said smiling at her. "That's what they call it in the Billiard Hall."

As she walked back to the shop she kept repeating the name to herself. She thought it had a ring to it, a name you could easily remember. When she told my father, he thought so too and they decided to get a new name board with "Sissymints" on it, to put over the shop window; but before this came the trip to the Blackpool illuminations.

Chapter Six

The Sunday they set off was overcast and looked like rain, and Cissie put on her best coat that she had recently treated herself to. It was a heavily checked affair with an imitation fur collar. She wore a black hat and carried a paper carrier bag with cheese sandwiches my mother had cut up the night before. The bus was full and they sat in the back seat which held five. A Mr. and Mrs. Platt from Card Street sat next to them. Mrs Platt was a regular customer of the chip shop and Mr. Platt, a jovial man, kept trying to amuse them but somehow couldn't quite manage it, and what was worse, when he lit his pipe it filled the back seat of the bus with a fug of smoke. That set Cissie coughing to such an extent that she was red in the face. When he saw this, instead of putting his pipe out, he began a long tale of how his mother used to mix a home made cough mixture and keep it warm on the hob for when they had coughs as children.

This developed into a story of what a good mother his mother had been, and how he'd sat with her when she was dying, and how his sister had never been near, yet no sooner had his mother died than she'd taken the mirror from over the mantlepiece which should rightly have been his. While he was telling this tale, Cissie was getting worse and my father tried to pull a bus window open but unfortunately it was stuck. Then just as matters were getting desperate Mr. Platt knocked his pipe out and Cissie went down to the front of the bus where the air was clearer.

When the bus finally drew up in Blackpool, Cissie got off, drew a deep breath of fresh air and gasped, "Thank God". The journey had been a nightmare. All she wanted was fresh air, and soon she got more than she needed, for the wind was very strong and blowing sheets of rain between the buildings. As they turned towards the shelter of a big public house a gust of wind nearly blew Cissie's hat off, and as they were all getting soaked, my father suggested they went into the public house. Cissie, was very bigoted against pubs, but was so discomforted she didn't argue until they were seated inside.

"I didn't come to sit in pubs all day, you know Leonard. I wish I'd never come at all. I shouldn't a let yer persuade me. Suppose I get laid up?"

"Persuade you! It was you as kept on about seeing the illuminations!" my father exclaimed.

"Oh shut up! We're here now I don't know how I survived that bus journey. My coat's soaked".

"You should a brought yer umbrella," my mother said.

"I shouldn't a come at all Lily," Cissie snapped.

They went on like this while they waited for the rain to abate. My father had a glass of beer, my mother a shandy, but Cissie refused to have anything. Then she said she felt cold.

"Have a drop of stout," my father suggested.

She vehemently refused at first, then changed her mind and had a port and lemon, which surprisingly managed to cheer her up. The rain stopped so they left the pub and hurried towards the promenade. It was still windy and the sea was wild with heavy waves crashing on the pavement. Cissie stared and shuddered. She had never in her life seen the sea in such a wild state and the nearness of it frightened her. How anybody dared to go out in a boat in such weather was beyond her understanding.

"My God Lily, just look, there's a ship out there." She pointed toward the horizon where a grey shape could barely be seen. "I wouldn't be on that for a thousand pound."

A gust of wind nearly blew her hat off again, so they made their way into the shelter of the Winter Gardens. Just as they went in through the main doors, a man in a bandsman's uniform was coming out and Cissie recognised him at once.

"Well, well, wonders never cease," he said. "It's the lady from the park isn't it?"

In the next few minutes there was a gabble of talk in which he introduced himself as Herbert Pepper.

"Pepper and Salt, we are only short of vinegar," my father said. This caused everybody to laugh.

The bandman said he'd come to a band contest in the Winter Gardens but his band was the last on the list to play. He said they had recently won third prize at a contest in Belle Vue, but their regular conductor had fallen ill. The man who was conducting them today had no idea, so they'd no chance of winning. He himself played the triple tongue cornet and could play a number of other wind instruments as well. Cissie was impressed and said how nice it must be to be so talented and how she wished she could do something more than frying chips.

Herbert Pepper look thoughtful. "It inner all it's cracked up ter be, banding isn't. It's a lot er work really for nothing. It's practice, practice, practice, but if yer do anything long enough, it turns to scrubbing. You know it's a funny thing, every time I come to Blackpool, I meet somebody from home. I've seen three blokes I know this morning." As he was saying this two more bandsmen in their blue uniforms came past and he waved to them. "Anyroad, it's nice ter meet you. I'll have ter call in your shop one of these days," he said as he moved away to catch up with the other two.

"Well well who'd a thought it, Salt and Pepper eh?"

"You've clicked there Cissie," my father laughed.

"Don't be so daft," Cissie snapped. "I want no man round me, I've seen enough misery in my life through men."

"You got yer money keep yer warm," my father said.

"You shut up about my money," Cissie snapped back.

She was in a better mood than when she'd just left the bus and was interested in everything in the Winter Gardens and the Tower Ballroom. When she saw the Tower from one of the streets directly below, my father told her that it swayed in the wind. She became afraid and made them hurry away. They went on a tram ride across the whole front and this pleased her greatly as she'd never been on a tram before. She marvelled at the sea, which was now a lot calmer, but when my father suggested that they go on the pier, she said she wouldn't got on it for a fortune. When they passed a theatre with an enormous portrait of George Formby on a poster over the foyer, she stopped and stared.

"Yer mean he's in there now?"

"Very likely; he's probably rehearsing," my father said.

"Oh it makes me feel funny to think he's in there, in the flesh. Oh I wish I could have seen the show," Cissie said, staring up at the poster.

"Why don't you stop overnight in a bed and breakfast. We'll look after the shop," my mother suggested.

Cissie at once turned on her. "What! I've got more on my plate than spending money on a bed I've never slept in when I've got a good bed at home. Oh no. It'erd want more than George Formby ter get me to stop a night in a place like this. I'll be glad for get on that bus, I'll tell yer. I should never have come. It's nothing but a catchpenny hole, this in't."

Later in the afternoon it started to rain and the wind began to blow again. As they walked among the deserted rides in the amusement park, looking up at the thousands of coloured light bulbs, the whole scene seemed tawdry and sad. Cissie became more miserable and flared up at the slightest remark blaming my father for her being there. When he kept protesting that it hadn't been his suggestion, it only made her more irritated.

"I should never have listened to yer. I should have had more sense. Mrs. Plimbley told me there were bugs in the bed where she stopped; I'm not surprised."

As she was saying this, they came to where a mechanical man in a glass case kept laughing and laughing as though he couldn't stop; and as they stared at him, it seemed he was laughing at them. At first Cissie shuddered with horror at the sight, but then began looking back at it with curiosity.

"Yer know Leonard, it puts me in mind of somebody only I just can't think who it is. Who does it put you in mind of Lily?"

My mother looked perplexed, but my father chipped in; "George Formby's drunken twin brother."

Cissie frowned. "Oh shut up, yer daft devil. I mean, really, who does it remind you of? Yer remember when me father used to come home drunk and bang his head on that mangle and me mother used ter lock him out? That puts me in mind of him. What was that song he used ter sing, you know. The song when yer laugh all the time?"

"He used ter sing Ben Bolt," my father said.

"No not that one, yer know, it was, like, laughing . . . ha! ha! ha! ha!"

"Oh yer mean the laughing policeman!"

"That's it!" Cissie laughed. "That man just reminded me of him. Oh Len it's nearly thirty years ago since he died. It make yer feel old dun't it?" She looked at him helplessly. "It used to terrify me when he sang that. I didn't like all that laughing. I thought he'd gone mad and that dummy's just the same. There's nothing funny about it. Mrs. Boot was telling me about her eldest sister, her went funny, you know, her's been locked away for years. When they go see her, her doesn't know 'em. Her just sits there staring at the wall in front of her. I think I'd sooner be dead than that."

"Oh for God's sake, shut up Cissie. Try to look on the bright side of things for a change There inna many as have got what you've got," my father said.

"I've had ter work hard for it," Cissie mumbled. "I sometimes think I've never had any pleasure in my life. It's been nothing but work, work, work."

She went on and on in this fashion as they walked back toward the town centre, keeping close to the shop fronts to shelter from the rain.

My father, now fed up, grumbled back at her. "We are supposed to be here to enjoy ourselves aren't we? At least I thought that was the general idea."

My mother who was linking arms with Cissie interrupted. "It 'erd a bin a lot better if the weather had a bin better, Cissie. There inna much pleasure at Blackpool if it's raining." As she was saying this she suddenly stopped and sniffed the air. "Yer know what I can smell?"

Cissie sniffed the air but looked puzzled, "I can't smell anything."

My father who was a few yards in front turned and sniffed himself "Fish!, I can smell fried fish!"

"Fish and chips! Yer should recognise that smell, Cissie," my mother laughed. "There you are, across the road, it's a fish and chip shop."

Cissie was all attention and after staring at the shop for a few seconds began to hurry across the road. The chip shop was a big double fronted premises covered entirely in green facing tiles, with the sign in black shiny lettering and electric light bulbs across the top of each letter. It was the biggest, most modern chip shop Cissie had ever seen and she stood absorbed for a few moments, taking in the wonder of it. Then without saying a word to my parents, she pushed the door open and went in and stood in amazement at the magnificence of the interior. It was beyond anything she could have imagined. There were four assistants smiling behind the counter in white aprons, wearing similar collars and ties. There must have been at least twenty tables, some set in little alcoves by the walls, also covered in green tiles. Across the back wall a number of tall mirrors made the place look much bigger than it was. On each of the tables she saw an identical cruet and over each table an electric light. She calculated at least twenty of them and then to crown all this, there was the great centre-piece of the chip fryer. It reminded her of the great Wurlitzer organ in the Town Hall. Until seeing it, she had naively imagined that the one in her shop was modern. but as she stared in wonder, she realised how paltry hers was. By comparison it was pitiful. This one was at least three times as big and instead of two frying pans, it had five, and as she could see no fire box, she imagined it must be fired by gas. There were a number of customers eating at the tables, with a waitress in a uniform attending to their needs. For a few moments, she stood and let the wonder of this great chip emporium sink in. Then she turned to my parents.

"My God Lily, did you ever see anything like this. It makes yer sick doesn't it? It must have a cost a pretty penny."

"I'll bet the overheads are enormous", my father said. "Look how much the fish is." He pointed towards a big menu board with all the prices on.

Cissie stared up. "Good God, fish and chips, two and six, tea and bread and butter sixpence, pudding, chips and peas, three shillings." She uttered these prices as though they were the beginnings of a prayer, then suddenly stopped. "You'd want a pound for three of you. It makes yer wonder how folks afford it," she said wonderingly.

"They'll pay anything when they're on holiday," my mother said.

Cissie suddenly looking miserable, replied tersely, "Taters only cost the same as back at home; fish should be a lot cheaper. Look at all them electric lights. The electric bill must be enormous."

Then my father said, "Well are we going to have anything or not? I could just fancy a fried fish."

My mother said, "I'm not paying that price for fish. I've got all the fish and chips I want at home."

"Anyroad, what about all them cheese sandwiches we cut up?" Cissie said.

"There's only a few left. He got in them on the bus," my mother replied.

"Oh our Len, you are a gutsing devil. Anyroad I didn't come Blackpool to buy fish and chips. You pair can please yerselves."

"I'm well aware we can please ourselves Cissie," my father said sarcastically, and the conversation between them began to get more fractious as they sat down at one of the tables, My mother and father decided to have a fried fish each and Cissie mumbling something to herself, ate one of the cheese sandwiches. But no sooner had she got it to her mouth than a waitress rushed across the shop and told her that eating food you'd brought into the shop yourself was not allowed and pointed to a notice above where they were sitting that indicated this. This made Cissie so angry that she sat nattering to herself about what a catchpenny hole Blackpool was, and how she'd known all along that it would be since she'd got up in the morning, and that folks had got more money than sense to pay the prices. This last was intended for my parents who were now eating their fish.

"Yer make me sick you do, our Len. You've always been the same. Yer always stuffing yerself with summat."

"Oh shut up Cissie, you've been pulling yer face all day. Why can't yer enjoy yerself like anybody else. Money, money, money. Yer getting worse. yer a bloody miser, woman!"

"Oh give over," my mother snapped. "Yer always the same, you two are, yer like cat and dog!"

Every now and then my father and Cissie had a row like this and being brother and sister, they often said very bitter things to each other and five minutes later, forgot it. On this occasion it was made worse by both of them being fed up and in strange territory.

"It's self, self, self all the bloody time, all yer think about is yourself. We can't help it if it's rained all day, it inna our fault," my father went on.

"Oh no, it never is your fault, you're always in the right," Cissie snapped.

"Give over!" my mother pleaded.

"Never mind 'give over', Lily. Her's been pulling her face all day, miserable bugger," he chuntered.

Cissie's face clenched in anger. "Don't worry Lily, I won't say any more," she said with as much dignity as she could muster.

"Our Phoebe's right," he was about to go on, but hearing Phoebe's name mentioned was more than Cissie could stand and remain silent.

"Phoebe! You should be ashamed of yourself how you've reared that girl. It's your fault as her's gone the way her has!"

"What d'yer mean?" my mother said angrily.

"Mean? Her's up and down with any rubbish. I heard tell of her getting out of some man's car at three o'clock in the morning. Her's the talk of the place with her hair coloured like a painted doll!"

"It's nothing do with you or anybody else what Phoebe does. Her life's her own. That shop's nothing but a gossiping hole. It's that Mrs. Caddy; her's no room for talk! Their Ivy's not all her should be."

At the mention of Phoebe's name, my father went quiet as the doings of his daughter were a source of great pain to him and only a few days before, there'd been a big row in our house about her goings on. He had used the very phrase "painted doll" as he was rowing with her, but as usual, Phoebe had got the better of him. He was always afraid of her leaving home and going further to the bad. She had now changed the colour of her hair to bleached blonde and dressed in what even my mother, who always tried to stand up for her, described as a "shameful way". She was working in a butcher's shop but was getting fed up with it and said the sight of that much raw meat turned her sick. But unknown to all of us at the time, she was up and down with the butcher's son, a feckless fool of a youth who liked showing off in his fancy car.

At the same time she was two timing him with one of her earlier admirers, a weakly, handsome taxi driver named Harry Twigg who was given to boasting of how many women he'd had in the back of his taxi. He'd once given Phoebe a black eye and she'd given him one back, and most nights they were together ended up with them at each other's throats. They'd finished with each other many times, but somehow, Twiggy as she called him, kept coming back and if she happened to be going out with another fella at the same time, she had no qualms about two timing him. Sometimes she had three or four blokes at the same time. My father said she was man mad and my mother tried hopelessly to believe she'd find somebody that suited her and settle down. This was about as likely as my Aunt Cissie giving her money to the Salvation Army.

Cissie knew that the mention of Phoebe's name always caused my father to go quiet and as they walked back to where the bus was parked, none of them spoke. But as they about to get on the bus, Cissie began to complain again.

"I hope we don't have to sit on the same seat as that man Platt. I couldn't stand another journey like that. I shall have ter ask somebody ter swap seats with me."

"It's all right with me, I don't think I could stand any more of your complaining," my father snorted. "I'm up ter here with yer already."

"Oh shut up Len," my mother said wearily.

As they got on the bus Cissie flopped down on the seat directly behind the driver and, by the look on her face, it was apparent she intended to stop there. My father and mother went to the back seat again and soon were joined by Mr. and Mrs. Platt carrying a bag filled with sticks of Blackpool rock. Mr. Platt's face was red and flushed and it was evident he had been drinking. Soon the bus filled except for two people, and after ten minutes or so, the driver kept looking impatiently at his watch. The other passengers began to get restless and there was some murmuring. Then Mr. Platt got off the bus and hurried to the gents in the bus station. He was still buttoning his trousers when he came out.

The driver angrily looked at his watch again and muttering something to himself, turned to the passengers. "I'll give 'em another five minutes and I'm off. I told 'em we were starting back at seven thirty. They'll be stuck in some pub. Some folks have no thought."

There were nods of agreement from some of the passengers. One woman said that the missing couple had missed buses back on day trips before. That decided the driver who started the engine and began to manoeuvre the bus out of the bus station. It was now dusk and as the bus turned from the side road on to the Front, the whole scene was flooded by millions of coloured lights. Every building was lit up and the tower glittered against the sky. It was what they had come to see, and as the passengers bent their heads to get a better look through the bus windows, Mr. Platt began to point out various pubs he'd been into. But when they passed the pleasure garden and the fun fair, the place was such a riot of colour and various imagery that it shut even him up.

Cissie was stunned by the scene, the like of which she'd never seen before and for a moment or two she took it all in. It was all too much for her; a world she didn't understand. The effigies of Mickey Mouse, Donald Duck and many other cartoon characters lit up with threads of coloured lights confused her. She didn't know who they were or what they represented. Blackpool was another world where everybody seemed to have plenty of money and kept spending it. This was deeply alien to her frugal nature; all those electric lights for instance. In that chip shop there must have been twenty or more on at once and it wasn't even dark. Surely they could have switched some off.

She kept trying to add it all up, but could make no sense of it. Then she began to feel dizzy. She shut her eyes and tried to calm herself down and in a few minutes when the bus had gone past most of the illuminations, she felt a bit easier. As she stared out of the bus window at the passing landscape she began to try to take stock of the whole day, and kept thinking about the contrast between the magnificent chip shop and her own little one.

Then the words of Mr. Tongue began to echo in her mind. "You've got to speculate to accumulate." She knew this was true, but she'd not spent anything on the shop for years. She was doing all right, better than all right, so why bother to alter anything? She found some comfort in this thought, but as she sat there, looking out of the bus window, the image of the marvellous chip fryer and all the green tiles kept recurring. As she saw the reflection of her face in the window glass, she began to imagine how her own shop could be changed from a simple fish and chip shop into something more like the one she'd seen in Blackpool.

First there would have to be a dining room; but there was no room for that. To start with, the shop wasn't big enough, unless she used the upstairs where she lived. This could become the dining room. But that would mean her living away from the shop. The thought of this had crossed her mind on a number of occasions recently. There was no doubt she could do with better accommodation for herself, but the thought of the expense had put her off the idea. It wasn't that she hadn't enough money to buy another house. She could buy a modern bungalow if it came to that. It was the thought of spending that deterred her.

But then, as the bank manager had said when they were talking about investments, bricks and mortar was the best investment of all. She wouldn't be spending her money if she bought another house. She'd really be investing it. She'd never thought of it this way before; but it was true; there was no getting away from from it. She'd enough money hidden in biscuit tins to pay cash for a house and the money she'd got hidden wasn't making her a penny in interest. But, if she had the shop altered, how would she keep it open during the alterations? Thoughts like this went round and round in her mind as the bus drove through the countryside, until she heard a number of complaints coming from the back seat and Mr. Platt came edging himself down the bus.

"It's no use I'm bosting. Once I start, it's all over. I shall have ter have a jimmy riddle."

He spoke to the driver who turned to him angrily. "Can't you wait till we get to the Romping Donkey? I'm calling there!"

Mr Platt indicated that he couldn't and there were a number of impatient noises from the passengers nearest the bus door as it drew to a stop and Mr. Platt edged himself down the steps.

"Some folks have no thought for others. They get a skinful of drink then have to keep peeing," a woman sitting behind Cissie said. The driver turned to her.

"You're lucky there's only one. There's usually a stream of 'em."

He started to go into a tale of some previous journey he'd made, when Mr. Platt began to maul himself up the bus steps again.

"I can't stop once I've started. As yer get older yer get a lot of bladder trouble," he wheezed.

The driver started off again and the bus windows became spattered with rain. It was now dark and after another half hour some of the passengers began to get restless as many of them didn't know if it was the driver's intention to stop at a pub. There was an excited murmuring as he pulled into the forecourt of the Romping Donkey and in a moment the bus was empty, except for Cissie who sat in her seat looking very glum. My mother and father had tried to get her to go into the pub and have a shandy, but she had angrily refused.

"I've been into one pub today and that will last me. I came for see the illuminations not sit in pubs. I'm surprised at you pair, I don't know how you afford it," she'd said.

After about fifteen minutes, some of the passengers began to board the bus again. When they were all on, the driver turned to them and looking at Mr. Platt shouted up the bus, "I'm not stopping again for anybody. I want to get back before closing time."

The bus swayed from side to side as he speeded through the lanes of Cheshire and soon they were back in familiar territory. When he pulled up in front of the meat market, Mr. Platt was the first off. "I'm bosting again," he said as he hurried away in the direction of the gentlemen's lavatories.

In the weeks that followed, the happenings that had occurred on the day out kept reaping up in Cissie's mind. For years before, all she'd seen from one week's end to the next were the same things; but the bus trip to Blackpool had been crammed with fresh visual experiences and as these kept recurring, they disturbed her.

Then something occurred which shook her life completely up. One day she was very troubled by her chest. She'd had a night disturbed by coughing, and next morning when my father saw her he said she looked like death warmed up. He suggested she should go to the Doctor's but she refused hoping that the coughing would go away. It didn't and by the time the shop opened she was worse. She decided to go to the Chemist's to see if he could recommend anything. She got her hat and coat on and made her way to the centre of the town where she'd decided to have a look round a haberdashery shop. Even as a young girl, she'd been fascinated by this shop, as it was filled with little counters, each connected by wires to a central pulpit. If the assistant serving at the counter needed some change she just put the money in a little container, and screwing a top on, pulled a lever. The container was dispatched along a wire to the pulpit where it was attended to by a cashier.

After she'd bought some buttons she spent half an hour looking round. When she stepped outside she heard the bell of the fire engine. At first she thought nothing about it but when the bell stopped she realised the fire wasn't far away. Even then it didn't trouble her as there were frequently fires in the town. She was about to enter the Chemist's when a boy came running up the High Street and as he passed she heard him shout, "It's the chip shop on fire!"

The shock of hearing this sent her reeling back against the shop door. She felt week; her legs trembled. "Oh my God," she gasped as she tried to compose herself. Then somehow she got enough strength to start making her way back. She hurried as best she could, mouthing something like a prayer. She didn't believe in God. She'd been to Sunday School as a little girl, but it had meant nothing to her. She did believe in something she'd no name for, something that brought more bad luck than good, and as she turned the corner into the Waterloo Road, she trembled throughout her whole being as she saw a fire engine outside her shop surrounded by a crowd of people.

Smoke was coming through the front door and one fireman was carrying a hose while another was standing on top of the fire engine pointing and shouting instructions. She saw my father and the girls who worked for her standing outside in their aprons. For a moment she stood transfixed, but when she saw a fireman open the upstairs window she began running as fast as she could. Pushing her way through the crowd, she ran into the smoke filled shop and made for the stairs. Before she'd gone a step she started to choke and cough with the smoke and a fireman dragged her outside. She was in a state of collapse, but the thought of anybody in her bedroom where her money was stacked away in big square biscuit tins drove her wild. She tried to get to her feet again, until my father held her back.

"Don't be so bloody silly, Cissie. The fire's out," he shouted at her.

It had been a fat fire, caused by some fault in the fire box. My father had for months told her that it needed attention, but as usual she'd put off doing anything about it; not that that stopped her from blaming him.

"I couldn't leave the shop five minutes without this. Whatever were you doing? God only knows what this lot's going cost. It'll ruin me," she shouted when the firemen had gone and she stood in the chaos of the smoke blackened shop.

"It won't bloody ruin yer woman, yer insured aren't yer," my father shouted back at her.

"It'll be months before we can open up again. Just look at this," she moaned staring up at what had been the ceiling, and was now just black laths. But for all her agitations at the state of the shop, the first thing she did when the firemen left was to make sure her biscuit tins in the bottom of her wardrobe were intact.

It was a local rumour that she kept money in a milk churn covered in fat. The truth was she kept half crowns, two shilling pieces, shilling pieces and sixpenny bits in separate biscuit tins in her wardrobe. Fortunately the fire brigade had reached the shop quickly enough to stop the fire spreading upstairs so her hoard of coins was safe.

Chapter Seven

The fat fire was a disguised blessing, as Cissie had to make her mind up about a lot of things that had been troubling her for the past year and it proved to be a turning point in both her life and the life of the chip shop. There was nothing else for it. Things would have to change although she was a woman who didn't like change. The first big alteration was caused by the bedroom ceiling falling in. She'd thought the upstairs was undamaged but when the fire officer came to examine the building a few days later, he'd poked at the ceiling with a stick and a lot of plaster had fallen down on her bed. She'd been angry with him at the time and had ordered him to stop jabbing with his stick as it was her opinion that he was doing the damage. But he'd taken no notice of her, and explained that the intense heat generated by the fire had weakened the ceiling.

This was a blow for her as it presented her with a fact she was reluctant to face. There was no getting away from it, she'd have to find somewhere else to live. My mother offered to put her up but we'd only two bedrooms and a little back room where I slept, and Phoebe flatly refused to share her room with her aunt and said she'd leave home if she came. So Cissie had to book into a bed and breakfast hotel up against the station kept by a Mrs. Flackett who was a regular customer at the chip shop. After Cissie had been there two days, she happened to be walking past the Town Hall when she bumped into Mr. Tongue. He was at once effusively sympathetic.

"Oh my dear, I was very upset to hear of the fire. It must have been terrible. How are you managing?"

He grasped her hand as he said this and squeezed it and as he listened to her tale of woe he kept making slight groaning noises as though he was actually experiencing her problems. When she came to the fact that she'd have to find somewhere else to live, his expression changed.

"Bricks and mortar my dear, you can't do better than bricks and mortar. We must attend to this matter at once. Now I have a very dear friend who's an expert in matters of property and I suggest I arrange for you to meet him. He'll put you right. He knows all the doors to knock on. Bed and Breakfast. My goodness Cissie, we can do better than that. You're a woman of substance. Leave it to me."

Within a few days, Mr. Tongue and his friend Mr. Cashmore Thorley, an estate agent had fixed Cissie up with a little terrace house in Leonora Street. It was in immaculate condition and had an inside toilet, a rarity in such streets in those days. More than anything this decided Cissie to buy the house, as the property was no more than half a mile or so from the chip shop. Mind you Mr. Thorley with the help of Mr. Tongue had all they could do to persuade her to buy the house. Mr. Tongue had to keep drumming into her that it was an investment and would increase in value as the the years went by.

Cissie had difficulty understanding this; money in the hand was what she understood. She could just comprehend that her money was safe in a bank, but to her when you paid for something with real touchable, countable money, handed it over to another person, it was gone, and like it or not, gone forever. This was how she understood things, and to sign over a big cheque, the biggest she'd ever signed, was a terrifying experience and she was trembling all over as she did it. To make matters worse, she was having the shop completely refurbished.

She had agonised over this decision, but realised there was nothing else for it and strangely, after she'd decided, a mood of recklessness came over her.

"I might as well be hung for a sheep as for a lamb," she said as she ordered the builder to gut the upstairs. She'd decided to turn it into a dining room.

The shop was boarded up and the work began. Every day from first thing in a morning to last thing at night she was there, seeing that the workmen worked and didn't sit smoking and drinking tea. After a while this caused a lot of resentment and there were a few rows. The foreman tried to explain that certain jobs couldn't be done till others had been completed. She found this difficult to believe and practically accused him and his men of malingering. He threatened to stop work altogether and told her to get herself another builder. This so frightened her, she kept her complaints to herself for a while.

Then, trouble blew up between her and Aaron, her next door neighbour, who continually cadging odd bits and pieces of material from the builders. One morning as she came in he was going out with two bricks they had given him. She accused him of pinching them and when the foreman told her he had given him them, she said he had no right to give him anything. She was paying for the job; all the materials were by rights, hers. At this the foreman told her to bugger off and meddle herself with her own business. She stormed back at him that it was her business. Then he fetched the owner of the building firm to her, a Mr. Porritt who somehow managed to smooth things over again.

For more than six weeks this went on till the basic building alterations were finished. The plasterers and the electricians came and she began to see the shape of the new chip shop slowly emerge which calmed her down a bit. Then one day, as she came through the door, she came face to face with Herbert Pepper, the bandsman only now he was wearing the white overalls of a painter and decorator.

"Well, well, we meet again," he said.

"Oh hello, Mr. Pepper," she beamed. "I didn't expect to see you here.

"Oh nobody expects ter see me," he joked. "I'm a will-o-the-whisk."

She was struck that he'd said 'whisk' instead of "wisp' and quickly wondered whether he'd meant to say it that way or not.

"A will of the what?" she asked.

For a moment he looked puzzled. "A will of the wisp, why?"

"You said a will of the whisk," she laughed.

"Did I? A slip of the tongue my dear, I'm always doing it, and how are you?"

"I'll be glad when this lot's done," she said looking at a new plastered wall with a hole from which protruded a number of wires.

"It won't be long now. Once we get the wallop on the walls. it'll begin to look sommat like."

It was true; since the wall had been painted, the smell of paint had freshened the whole place up. After a few days Herbert Pepper's cheery attitude began to affect Cissie and instead of her usual antagonism toward the workmen, she began to have a cup of tea at snapping time with them and got to know many of their names. Herbert seemed to calm a lot of her anxieties. Even amid the banging and hammering that went on most of the day he managed either to whistle or sing some piece of recognisable music and she got to know a lot about him.

He was fifty six years of age and had one son called Norbert. His wife who died six years earlier had wanted to call the boy Herbert after him, but he didn't want two Herberts in the family so they'd settled for Norbert. He'd reared his son himself. It had been difficult with him going to work in the day and band practice at night, but he'd managed it. Banding was very important to him, as music played a big part in his life. He'd been a member of the Co-op band since it's inception and was recognised in the world of brass bands as being one of the best triple tongue cornet players in the county. He could also play a number of other instruments and that was why his top lip was slightly deformed.

One day, as he had promised, he brought his cornet to give the lads a bit of a tune at snapping time. As they all sat round drinking mugs of tea he carefully lifted it out of it's case, tried a few trills, then began to play a tune Cissie had vaguely heard before. She thought it was very beautiful. All the workmen clapped or grunted their appreciation and Cissie thought what a gentleman Herbert Pepper was. Soon after she happened to mention that she was about to do some papering at her house. At once he offered to come and help. When she told my mother and father this, they both laughed and said she'd clicked, and began to joke about her having a fancy man. She took this in good part although it had never crossed her mind that Herbert was any more than a friend. But when my father took the joking a bit further and suggested that he may be after her money, she became furious. The mention of her money was anathema to my auntie.

"Don't you worry yourself about my money Leonard; you are always on about it. It's nothing do with you or anybody else what I've got or haven't got. I'll look after what's mine. Never forget that Leonard, I'd nothing when I started out, like you. Whatever I've got is mine and I intend to keep it. I've worked hard enough for it."

This provoked my father to needle her back and he said dryly, "Well Cissie, yer can't take it with yer. What's going to happen to it when you pop yer clogs?"

He'd made similar remarks before and they always irritated her. "Don't let that worry you Leonard; I don't let it worry me," she retorted.

During the refurbishing of the shop, talk of money had cropped up more than usual between them as she had refused to pay his wages while the shop was shut and he'd had to sign on the dole.

"D'yer think I'm made of money? You've paid your stamps haven't you. Yer entitled to the dole. I wish I was. How much d'yer think this lot's costing me? Money, I've got no money; it's cost me every penny I've saved. I'm earning nothing and you want me pay yer wages for doing nothing," she'd said angrily.

For weeks there'd been a bruised silence between them, but as the work on the shop came to an end and the cleaning up process began, she started to pay his wages again and in the excitement at the new premises, the bitterness faded away.

The shop front was still boarded up, but inside the building was completely transformed. The upstairs, which had been two bedrooms and a little back room was now one long dining room covered in green tiles, similar to the one she'd seen at Blackpool. Herbert, who seemed as thrilled by the shop's appearance as she was, said it was it's green glory and kept suggesting new names to call it. One "Chip Ahoy", another "The Golden Chip". He regularly had flights of fancy and began to irritate my father who started to call him "Oily Herbert". But Cissie admired him She said he cheered her up, which took some doing.

One day he brought his son Norbert to see the shop and my father disliked him on sight. He was a tall fair haired youth with a moustache the colour of pigs bristles and watery blue eyes that slid from side to side as he took everything in. No sooner was he inside the building than he acted as though he had a perfect right to be there; and what angered my father most was that he called Cissie, 'Cissie', as though he had known her ages.

"He's a hard faced cheeky bugger out for what he can get," my father said.

All these irritations were forgotten in the excitement of the opening which Cissie advertised in the local paper. And when the builders hoardings were finally pulled down, groups of people stood on the other side of the road admiring the smart exterior, as well they might, for the shop front gleamed and made the surrounding premises look squalid. The window of the dining room was particularly remarked on as it was made of frosted and stippled glass with a pattern of the rising sun's rays spread across the window. Cissie had chosen simple black glossy letters for the sign, "Sissymints", across the front and these stood out sharply against the green tiles. The whole effect drew many congratulatory comments.

Mr. Tongue, who'd come down specially to see it immediately ran across the road and started pumping Cissie's hand.

"Oh my dear, you've surpassed our wildest hopes. This is truly magnificent. It is without doubt the smartest shop in this city. It's a great credit to you Cissie. You must be very proud. I must say, I myself feel proud, to have had in my small way, something to do with it."

All the excitement and the smell of the paint began to upset Cissie's lungs. She developed a touch of bronchitis and began to worry about being ill for the opening.

"I'll be glad when it's all over and we can get back to normal. It's getting me down, this lot," she gasped to my father on the day before the opening as he was lighting the gas under the new chip machine which looked a bit like a Wurlitzer organ. He'd lit it a number of times before but couldn't quite regulate the heat and was getting worried. Then Norbert who happened to overhear him asked to look at the book of instructions that had come with the machine. After reading them he proceeded to make an adjustment to what was called a timing switch and the problem was solved.

Cissie was very impressed by this though my father was privately furious. "He's a big headed young bugger. Our Cissie make me sick. It's Herbert this and Herbert that and now it's Norbert as well," he growled to my mother.

"You mark my words, he's after summat that man. I could tell as soon as I saw him," my mother said.

"Oh I knew that, I'm not daft woman. He's after feathering his own nest, Pepper is,' my father replied bitterly. "After all we've done, all these years for her. Waited on her hand and foot! Stood all her snide remarks and kept our mouths shut. Oh it makes my blood boil when I think about it."

"She's never appreciated what you've done for her. She's always had you 'Jack at a pinch'. You've never stood up to her," my mother said, her face twisted with bitterness.

"Oh shut up woman," my father snarled, as when my mother started going on in this way there was no stopping her.

"Her'd look well if you didn't go in tomorrow wouldn't her? There's neither her nor none o'them others could fry them chips in that new machine. I can just see it; hundreds of customers and no chips."

It was true. Cissie had not attended to the frying of the chips for years. She'd always sat by the till.

"All her thinks about is money, and it's silly buggers like us as have earned it for her. Oh it makes me sick when I think about it."

She went on like this for a long time, but first thing in the morning next day she was there with a white apron on as excited as anybody else as they prepared to open the shop. Cissie went to unlock the front door trembling with excitement. They could see through the front window a queue had formed outside, but their excitement turned to dismay as the first customer to cross the threshold was a local character known as Klondyke, a tramp like figure often seen picking up fag ends from the gutter or mumbling to himself around the town. He was dressed in what looked like an old army coat with a piece of rope tied round his waist. He had a balaclava hat on his head, his face was unshaven and filthy and as he shambled in, a groan went up from all behind the counter.

He'd been known in the past to attempt to lead public processions. When the band was about to strike up, the boys brigade, the womens' services, and the various chapels, had assembled to begin a procession through the city, Klondyke would step out of the crowd, and to roars of encouragement from the rougher end of the population, he would signal the procession to start and march in front of it.

When the Police attempted to stop him, he'd always shout in a loud voice, "Is this the King's highway? Tell me that constable?"

If the constable answered, Klondyke would shout "Get out of the way and let an honest Englishman pass."

Being the first customer of the chip shop was evidently in Klondyke's mind as something of the same order, but there was nothing they could do about it so they served him as quick as they could hoping he'd go away with his bag of chips. But no. As soon as he'd got them he began to make his way upstairs to to the dining room. The shop was now full, and they'd as much as they could do serving, so just had to get on with it and try to forget about him and what he was up to in the dining room upstairs.

For the rest of the day, the shop remained so busy, anybody serving behind the counter hardly had time for a cup of tea. There were eight of them working flat out. Cissie as usual at the till, my father frying the chips, my mother and three other girls serving behind the counter and carrying trays of food up to the crowded dining room. Throughout, Pepper was helping in the back room, cleaning potatoes and cutting up fish.

He was helped by an old man with a hare shorn lip, named Potts, who was the husband of Mrs. Potts, the best customer of a Public House called "The Star". He suffered with his heart and on a number of occasions during the opening day, his face and lips turned purple with the effort of carrying buckets of peeled potatoes, but everybody was so busy they hadn't time to take notice of such things. As he said to his wife, when he got home, he could a dropped dead and folks were so busy, they 'd a just stepped over him.

There had never been such a day in a chip shop in that town before, a gala day, a day they'd remember for the rest of their lives. It went on till just after midnight when Cissie decided enough was enough and ordered my father to lock the front door, which he had some difficulty doing as there were still people waiting outside. Everybody in the shop was completely exhausted and the place that had been shining and new in the morning was a shambles. The dining room was in a state of chaos with each table full of dirty plates, vinegar bottles on the floor, salt cellars stolen, the leatherette on one tip up seat ripped open and worst of all, somebody had managed to draw a crude image of a naked woman on the front window.

When Cissie saw the mess she stood for a second, stunned, then she began to rave. "The dirty swine, they are like pigs! They deserve nothing but troughs."

She was so upset by it my father had to steady her as she went back down the stairs. Although on the point of collapse, she wanted to start cleaning the mess up there and then, but everybody shouted their disagreement. Herbert Pepper produced a bottle of sherry and when they were all in the back room, one of the girls washed some pop glasses and he announced that he would say a few words. My father groaned aloud, as Herbert poured a little sherry into each of the glasses then, wiping the sweat from his forehead, he lifted his glass and began.

"I think it's right for someone to speak on this auspicious occasion. It very rarely occurs in anybody's life for a dream to come true, but in Miss Cissie Salt's, it has. As we stand here among the dream, I'm sure that it has not been without great efforts on her part that this has been accomplished, and I raise my glass to a remarkable woman."

Some of them murmured their assent to these sentiments, but my father's jaw clamped together angrily as Herbert went on.

"For this, ladies and gentlemen is sacred ground. Do you realise what we have been doing today? We have been consecrating a temple to the chip."

He was about to go on in this flowery way, but Cissie began to cough and Mr. Potts asked for the back door to be opened as he couldn't get his breath. Herbert's speech petered out, they all began to get their hats and coats on, and the serving girls went home. Cissie went back in the shop and emptied the till. She'd emptied it once earlier in the evening but it was now cram packed full again. She never allowed anyone near her as she did this. On one occasion Herbert Pepper put his head in and shouted something about 'counting the loot'.

Cissie frowned and shouted irritatedly back at him, "Would you mind keeping quiet, Mr. Pepper while I attend to this matter."

He shut up at once and began to get his coat on, just as Mr. Potts, who'd been standing at the open back door trying to get some fresh air in his lungs began to gasp again. It was apparent the day had been too much for him and my mother sat him a chair.

"I'll be all right if I can get me breath," he said, but his face had now a very unhealthy sallowness about it and my mother looked worried. Cissie came in carrying the bag of banknotes which they took each night to the night safe at Lloyds Bank. Seeing the state Mr. Potts was in, she was very concerned and there was a lot discussion about what they should do. My father and mother always accompanied Cissie as bodyguards to the bank, but as Mr. Potts lived in the same direction as their house, she suggested that they help him home. Herbert Pepper, summing this situation up, jumped in by offering to accompany Cissie to the Bank, and after a few moment's kerfuffling, when my father tried to find some other arrangement, Cissie decided she'd be quite safe with Herbert. My father with a face as black as thunder and muttering angrily to himself said a curt good night to Cissie and Herbert Pepper, and walking on either side of Mr. Potts, they made off into the night in the direction of home.

No sooner had they guided him to his front door a few streets away than my father exploded with anger. "That smarmy bugger! Did you ever see anything like that? She's as soft as a bloody brush, our Cissie is. Why a blind man can see through that two faced sod."

Well what could we do? Mr. Potts looked like a dead man warmed up," my mother interjected.

Ignoring this, my father raged, "Let him bloody have it! Let the soft bugger wheedle his way in. Did you see his face as he said good night? I'll bet he's laughing his bloody head off."

"Oh shut up Len, you'll only upset yourself," my mother whined. "Her'll see through him before long. There's neither him nor anybody else er'll get a penny of her money while her's still alive."

"But what happens when anything happens to her? After all the years I've put in there. It's me as done the hard work. Any bugger can sit counting money at the till. Take today for instance, I've worked me guts out in front of that fryer. Sweat's poured off men and never a word of thanks. Oh no it's all Cissie; always has been."

"Oh shut up Len, for God's sake yer only upsetting yerself."

They were just turning into their street when she said this, and the street lamps on one side were all lit, but for some reason, the ones on the other side were out, and they could hear somebody shouting and swearing in the darkness. My mother held on tighter to my father's arm. When they got closer they could see the figure of a man in his shirt sleeves taking a fighting stance, and threatening one of the gas lamps. At once they recognised it. It was Little Fitz, a regular customer of the chip shop. He had been in the shop earlier in the night and was now quite clearly drunk and as they passed him on the other side of the street, they could hear him shouting. "Get yer fists up, come on. Put 'em up." Then he began to dance up and down like a boxer, advancing and ducking, then striking out with his fists at the lamp post. He was like a little dervish. They had seen him in this state many times before as he was one of the street's characters.

My father shouted across to him, "Jack Dempsey's after thee Fitz."

He stopped his shadow boxing, waved, staggered across to them and giving them the thumbs up sign with both thumbs, he spluttered, "It's the finest chip shop I've ever set foot in. It's champion, champion, champion." And that was how the first day at the new chip shop came to an end.

Chapter Eight

I have purposely kept myself out of this little history, as the main stem of the story is the chip shop and it's proprietor, my Auntie Cissie. But as both my parents were directly involved in all it's doings and my name is Salt, I feel I should now brush in a few details about my own life and others of my generation. The story up to now has brought us to the late nineteen thirties, just before the War. I was in my late teens, a bit of a misfit, unable to settle at anything. I had already had seven or eight jobs and hated most of them. The only thing I really enjoyed was going to the pictures and mooching round the pubs after I'd come out. This angered my father who often rowed with me about my aimless way of living and said I'd never amount to anything, though his real bitterness was directed at my sister, Phoebe, who seemed to take delight in angering him.

If he was shaving in front of the back kitchen mirror, she'd stick her head in front of his to put lipstick on. If he was mending his shoes with the iron foot, she'd be painting her toe nails in front of him. I can still remember after all these years, the viciousness of the rows when she came in late. My mother used to plead with him to leave her alone, but truth to tell, she was as worried about her as he was, for Phoebe was always a law unto herself and frightened of nobody. She'd been the same as a little child. I can vaguely remember hearing her squeal till she was red in the face if she couldn't get her way. It was the same when she was at school. She'd fight like a hell cat with other girls in the school yard. It was as though she liked being the centre of trouble. Trouble there was plenty as she grew older, for she grew from being a bony knee'd girl with long straggly hair, into a shapely young woman. She had high cheek bones, and big dark, almond eyes and her wild hair became long and lustrous overnight.

Although she was my twin sister, I'd never felt close to her. We were so different in both temperament and body. It was as though the different features that ran through the family, which hadn't come to much before in any of the rest of Salts, for none of the men by any stretch of the imagination could be called handsome, and none of the women beautiful, in Phoebe had gelled together perfectly. For our Phoebe was a beauty. There was no doubt about it, she was the Carmen of mean streets and as could be expected, the local Romeos were soon hanging round our back gate; as my father said, "like flies round a jam pot". But when I think back on his anger, I realise some part of it may have been jealousy. When Phoebe was a little girl she'd been the apple of his eye. He'd always put her on his knee and called her his little papoose. It was only when she grew out of childhood and became a nubile young woman that he changed. All this was happening about the same time as the shop was spruced up. I was working at a little side street tin plate works and knocking up and down with a girl named Doris Fairbanks. I used to kid her about having the same initials as Douglas Fairbanks, as at that time we did most of our courting in the pictures. I did not take this affair seriously and often used to go out with other girls as Doris did with other blokes.

One night I went to call for her at the council house where she lived. She had three sisters, one of whom was named Alma. I fancied her more than Doris, and on this night it was Alma who came to the door. She said Doris had gone out and wouldn't be long so she invited me in. She wasn't dressed up and had no make up on. When she sat down I could see her stockings were slack. Then as she flopped backwards in an armchair, I caught more than a glimpse of her naked thighs. She was alone in the house, as both her parents had gone to Prestatyn for a week's holiday and as she sprawled lazily in the chair, I could tell by the way she was half smiling at me that she was enjoying the situation. I knew, she knew I'd been looking up her legs, and she knew I fancied her, which I did very much. As I sat there the spit dried up in my mouth. I cannot remember what she said and what I said, but after what seemed ages, she got up and stood in front of the mirror over the fireplace and began to attend to her hair. As she lifted her arms I could see her armpits and how her breasts pointed upwards through her blouse and the shadows of her nipples. Then she turned sideways. I could see the slight rise of her stomach and the way her thighs pressed forward under her skirt, and what's more I knew she wanted me to see her in this way. I knew she was flaunting herself and I was aroused. At that moment I wanted more than anything to put my arms around her and press her body against mine, to feel the rise of her stomach against my body.

A few minutes later, I heard the back door open and Doris came in looking flushed. She was very surprised to see me and said she'd been doing one of her mate's hair. I later learned that this was a lie and she'd been seen with another bloke, but it didn't trouble me as my lust was more aroused by her sister Alma and I could hardly sleep for thinking about her body. One night as I was walking home after a few drinks in a number of pubs, I was passing a bus stop when I saw Alma get off. She was dressed up and had all her war paint on. Her eyes were dark ringed with eyeshadow and her lips were red gashes across her face. She was wearing high heels and a skirt above her knees.

No sooner had I seen her than I was all of a tremble and almost without a conscious decision, found myself hurrying to get near her. When I caught up with her I bumped into her pretending it was an accident. She turned and smiled into my face. I asked if she'd mind my walking her home. She indicated that I could, and with my heart pounding in my chest I walked beside her through the streets leading to her house. I was again dry mouthed and couldn't find anything to say and neither could she. Then as we turned a corner, she bumped into me. No sooner had our bodies touched than I felt the electricity between us. A moment later we passed a dark entry. I manoeuvred her into it and we started to kiss and embrace. Her response was immediate and total. She pressed her thighs against mine and opened her mouth and it was apparent at once she expected me to take her there and then. But a few minutes later, as matters were getting beyond control, a light came on at the end of the entry and I heard a man shout angrily, "Is that you Vera?"

Like a flash, Alma pushed me away and stepped back in the street and I followed her all of a fluster, and as we hurried away, I cursed. When I attempted to get her to go down another entry, she refused. "Oh no, not again duck, not tonight, you really got me going, I'm all of a tremble inside," she said looking directly into my eyes. Then she gave me a quick little kiss and left me at the end of her street and hurried toward her house.

In the next few days, what was attempted in the entry was accomplished a number of times and it was Alma who often instigated it. I found she was insatiable, much more passionate than I was and soon I was besotted with her. All we seemed to live for was sex. Whenever we were together, if I didn't start matters, she would. Where we were going was less important to her than where we were going to do it, and after a few weeks this began to get a bit too much for me, and I started to think how nice it would be just to stand at a bar and have a few half pints without a sex hungry woman in attendance.

Alma was on the dole at this time, and one day I heard my father say that Aunt Cissie needed another girl to serve behind the counter, as one of her girls had left. I told Alma, and mentioned her to him. He'd no idea of how things were between us so she got the job, and that was the real reason I became a regular attender of my Aunty Cissie's chip shop. I had to be careful not to show my feelings too obviously as I knew that

Alma

Cissie was very stern with the girls who worked behind her counter and would allow no chatting up by fellas at all. "This isn't the monkey run," she'd say to any of them who tried it, so I used to attend to the chip shop pretending I hardly knew Alma. When Cissie asked me to help out on three of the busiest nights of the week, I thought I might as well. So I started carrying plates of food up the stairs to the dining room as the girls used to complain about some of the customers up there making filthy suggestions and pinching their behinds. One became so angry, she tipped a trayful of food over a lout's head. This led to such a shemozzle that Cissie had to call the police, a thing she hated doing. Usually her fury was enough to deal with any trouble that cropped up and on busy nights it often did.

Cissie tried hard to keep the drunks out, but sometimes she couldn't tell they were drunk till it was too late and they were upstairs. She put a number of these louts on a black list but often it wasn't drunks who caused the trouble but groups of youths trying to impress girls. Cissie got so angry with one of them, a potato headed lout called Crud, that she caught hold of him by his hair and tried to drag him downstairs. He fought back and being much stronger than her, began to hurl her round the table. But her fury was such that she managed to hang on. My father and Herbert Pepper got the youth out of the shop. They wanted to fetch the Police but she wouldn't let them although the struggle had exhausted her to such an extent that she had to lie down.

I'd no strength left. I'd a killed him if I could a got me breath. If I see him in here again, he'll get a cup of hot fat in his face. We'll see what a big ike he is then."

This violence was nothing out of the ordinary for any of us who worked in the shop. We had all been reared in the streets of the town and were familiar with the kind of characters it produced. We knew all the nut cases, the hard men, the ten tonners, the monstinks, the loud mouths, the fools, and they knew us. We knew when there was real danger and when it was just loud mouthed bluff. Certainly Cissie wasn't afraid of anything that happened in the shop. Her deepest fear was burglars pinching the money she'd stored in her house, as it was empty for many hours a day.

I could never understand why she kept money round her instead of banking it with her other takings. It was as though the silver coins were more real to her than the notes she paid into the bank. I used to imagine her sitting alone in her bedroom with the biscuit tins open, letting the half crowns fall through her fingers, cackling like a witch. By now she was beginning to look a bit like one, as she'd had the last of her teeth out. Although she'd bought a set of false teeth, she hardly ever wore them; she said they made her heave. My sister Phoebe sometimes gave an imitation of her that was so good, it even made my father laugh. She'd suck her cheeks in and hang her hair loose and sit at the table drooling as she pretended to count the takings.

At times like these, when there'd been no rows Phoebe would dance and sing round the house. She knew all the words of every song she'd ever heard and she'd dance her way upstairs, and dance her way down, like something she'd seen on the pictures. These moods only happened occasionally, but when they did, it made me wonder about her Jeckyll and Hyde personality. It was as though there were two separate people inside her. My father used to say when she was good, she was very, very good and when she was bad she was horrid.

It was Phoebe who first set doubts in my mind about Alma. When she saw how it was between us she said, "I should watch out boy. You could get your fingers burnt there."

At first I didn't understand what she was on about but soon I began to have my own doubts about Alma. There were times when I knew she was lying but didn't pursue the matter as I was so besotted with her. She knew she'd only got to flicker her eyelashes and I'd stop any of my jealous questioning. Once she stood me up, and the next time I saw her she was wearing a silk scarf round her neck. We were on a bus at the time and I saw the scarf slip and I was sure there was a love bite on her neck. I knew it wasn't me that had made it because she was very particular about me kissing her neck. I was soon hollowed out with doubts, and filled with jealousy to such an extent that I asked her about it. She was highly indignant that I should doubt her at all and the rest of the night she sulked and for days didn't let me even kiss her.

One night after the chip shop closed, I was up in the dining room cleaning the tables before going home. Cissie was at the till, my father was doing something in the back room and the other girls had gone home, when Alma came creeping upstairs. She put her arms around my neck and began kissing me passionately in a way I knew meant that she wanted me to make love to her there and then. I tried to push her away and whispered something about somebody coming and catching us at it, but she had thrown caution to the winds. She wanted it and began to unbutton my trousers. Then she whispered something to me that I will not write down as it was crude sexual language that we used between us when we were in this state. It aroused me at once and so we made love there and then on a table I'd just cleaned.

It was soon over and when we'd straightened our clothes I whispered "I'll bet it's the first time anybody had it in here."

"Oh I don't know, I'll bet Cissie and Herbert are at it all the time. Perhaps her has a pinch of snuff fer get her going," she laughed. For some reason I felt a snatch of anger at her saying this, as the thought of Aunty Cissie having anything to do with sexual matters was grotesque and certainly not true.

This streak of coarseness in Alma sometimes dismayed me. When it was between us, privately and sexually, it excited me, but when it came out as it often did as dirty jokes or sexual innuendo, I used to protest about it, and then she'd accuse me of hypocrisy. "You're two bloody faced you are, Mr. Goody Goody. Sometimes you're a lot worse than me, a lot worse than anybody I've ever known." She'd spit this out at me.

"And you've known some," I'd retort sarcastically.

"It's nothing to do with you who I've known before I started going with you. You don't own me," she'd snap back angrily and usually this led to a coolness between us and at such times I'd wish I was free and up and down the pubs on my own again. But it was no use. If we ever rowed, which we often did to such an extent that we didn't speak for a day or two, it was always me who broke the silence. Then she'd make me grovel. My father called me a bloody fool and I knew he was right, but I couldn't get away from her. Sometimes she'd taunt me by saying she was going to leave home and get a job in London or some other big city, as she was sick of living in the dump this town was. Other times she'd mention some fellow she'd seen who'd really taken her fancy.

"Oh he was really something, and I know he fancied me. I could feel his eyes all over me, oooh."

Sometime she'd push me too far and I'd explode and tell her to bugger off and go with who ever she fancied. When this happened, she'd just look at me as though she was sorry for me, sign, and say something like "Don't worry duck, I've got one lover and I don't want two." Then she'd ask me if I loved her and when I always said I did she'd look doubtful. "How do you know?"

"I know because I know," I'd reply.

"Are you sure, because I'm not always sure I love you. sometimes I do, sometimes I don't. Sometimes you're horrible, really horrible and I hate you." She'd tease me in this way and I'd feel like a fool. But fool or not, when her voice changed and

she'd whisper some sexual remark, all banter would stop and
we'd soon be at it again. It was to me a battle that I was always
losing. She was always in command. If she wanted to be
awkward, we'd be awkward. If she wanted to be lovy-dovy, we'd
be lovy-dovy. I felt helpless and hated it and wished I'd never set
eyes on her. I'd often thought what bloody fools the blokes were
as lusted over Phoebe, and now I suspected I was as big a fool as
any of them.

While I was trapped in this affair, Europe was moving
toward another war, though as far as I was concerned, it was all
happening somewhere on another planet. It had nothing to do
with me. This was the same in the chip shop most days. Some
customer or other would mention Hitler and go on about
something they'd read in the papers or heard on the wireless, but
it didn't seem to register with Cissie or anybody who worked
there. Life was too intense in the shop for the outside world to
interrupt. Politics were never mentioned. The till was the only
politics that Cissie knew or wanted to know.

One day there was the noise of some heavy rattling vehicle
outside on the main road and when my father looked through the
window he saw what he thought were a number of tanks going
down the Waterloo Road. They were actually Bren Gun Carriers,
but he didn't know the difference, and later in the day a number
of soldiers came into the shop and had fish and chips in the
dining room.

Alma served the soldiers, and was full of it when I saw her
later that day. She said she wouldn't mind joining up with the
women's Army. To her the prospect of war was exciting, and when
I thought about it, it was to me. If it hadn't been for Alma, I
would have seriously thought about joining up. When I
mentioned this to her she was all for it, which disappointed me.
When I asked her if she wouldn't miss me, she became something
I"d never known her be before — patriotic!

"We'll all have to make sacrifices for our country," she said,
looking as serious as she could manage.

"What sacrifices are you going to make?" I asked
sarcastically.

"Oh you'd be surprised," she said looking straight through
me as though I wasn't there.

From that day on, the rumours of war, and how it would
affect us began to seep into the shop. My father predicted that
Hitler would stand no chance against the might of the British
and French armies. He'd never get past the Maginot Line.
Although he'd never had any military experience, my father soon

began to speak authoritatively on military matters. This irritated Herbert Pepper, as he had been in the Territorials in his younger days and had at least fired a rifle.

"You've got to have experience of war to know what you're talking about," he said pompously.

"I suppose you've got it," my father smiled sardonically.

"Well I've worn the King's Uniform, if that counts for anything," Herbert retorted.

"This isn't playing soldiers, it's real war I'm talking about Herbert, not bloody boy scouts."

"Boy Scouts! You want to spend a weekend in winter under canvas with about a dozen or more blokes in the same tent; making yer tea in a bucket filled with matchsticks; lugging a bloody great pack on you back over the Brecon Beacons; Boy Scouts! Oh, the territorials er'll be the first to go France if this lot blows up. They'll be the first. They always 'ave," Herbert said angrily.

"They'll be no use mate. This war will be different. It's all bombing nar," my father retorted.

They had dozens of arguments like this as the news of the impending war was reported by the papers and on the wireless. It became the main item of conversation between them. My father couldn't abide Herbert, and Herbert was not too fond of my father. The arguments about the war became a battleground they could air their mutual dislike of each other on.

"He's a big headed bugger, Pepper is," my father used to say when he got home.

My mother at the time hardly ever went to the chip shop, as she was always ill with some women's ailment that never seemed to get better. Little by little she became an invalid and could do less and less round the house. She went to the doctors, and he sent her to the Hospital. She had an operation, and for a few weeks we thought she was getting better. But I noticed her eyes seemed to be deeper and darker in her head than they'd ever been before, and her cheek bones became more prominent. I will not go into this matter any further as it was all misery for the next few months. One morning she was in such pain that my father fetched the doctor, who rang for an ambulance. She died in Hospital the next day.

A few days later, we had the funeral in the morning as Aunty Cissie had to open the shop at dinnertime. When we were getting into the funeral car I caught a glimpse of an anchor tattooed on our Phoebe's leg just above the knee. I was about to question her about it but I held back as I realised what a row it would cause when my father saw it. As the funeral cars drove up the Moorland Road towards the cemetery, I just sat and stared through one window and Phoebe sat staring through the other. My emotions since the day my mother had died seemed to have dried up. I felt a numbness, had no appetite, and all I wanted was for the funeral to be over. I had only been to one other funeral in my life, and had only seen one dead person before. When I saw my mother in her coffin, I was shocked to see how small she was. Her silver blue face was no bigger than a little thin doll's. I was repulsed by the sight of death and as the hearse just a few yards ahead of us drove slowly forward, I kept thinking of the soles of my mother's feet inside her coffin.

My attention was then taken by the big tip and the trucks going round and round tipping their dirt down from the aerial ropeway. I remembered when I was a boy, climbing to the top in winter with another lad, who was killed on his bike a few months later. The image of Elijah Mumford, the keeper of the tip came to my mind, as when we reached the top, we heard a shout from below and saw Elijah, dressed in what looked like filthy coal bags, shaking a knobstick at us. We ran round the other side of the tip to avoid him, but when we got to the bottom he nearly caught us. As I passed in the funeral motor, in my minds eye I could see him clearly, a fearful figure covered in coal dust, his lips and tongue pink and wet with spit, the whites of his eyes gleaming like a madman's.

"I'll bloody belt yer if I lay me hands on yer," he shouted as we skidded and ran down the tip on on to the road. All this came into my mind as the cortege came slowly up the hill and it brought a sense of the transience of life to me.

Elijah Mumford was dead years ago. That lad that was with me was dead years ago. My mother lay dead in her coffin a few yards in front of me and a few minutes later as the coffin was lowered into the grave in the churchyard, I saw a look of anguish on my Aunty Cissie's face. It was as though the sight of the hole had forced her to realise that someday she'd have to go and leave all her money behind.

A few hours after my mother had been buried, Cissie had no sooner opened the shop than a woman named Forshaw came in. A slack, bag-faced creature, with a slight moustache across her long loose mouth, she was breathless and agitated as she exploded with complaint. She'd bought a meat and potato pie and chips the day before, and when she'd arrived home and was about to swallow the first mouthful of pie, she'd felt her false teeth scrape against something. She'd spit the food out and found a nail in it and what's worse, a number of little black dots, which her husband said were mouse droppings. What would have happened if she'd a swallowed that lot, she kept saying.

As Cissie listened to this her face clouded with worry. She'd seen such cases reported in the paper and knew this sort of thing could damage the reputation of her shop. She tried to pacify the woman explaining that although she sold the pies as home made, she actually bought them from a Baker named Bowcock. She'd get in touch with him at once. She took the woman's address and said she'd see into the matter, but Mrs. Forshaw left the shop muttering about reporting it to the Health Inspector. No sooner had she gone than Cissie got in touch with Mr. Bowcock, who came from his bakery looking very worried.

Shaking his head he said, "I can't understand it. A nail yer say? What sort of nail?"

"I don't know what sort of nail, her didn't say. It doesn't matter what sort does it? A nail's a nail," Cissie snapped. "You'd better go see her about it."

"See her," Mr. Bowcock repeated the words as though it was the last thing in the world he'd thought of doing.

"Yes, you'll have ter see her won't yer."

"You mean I should go and see her," he said again.

He was a round pale faced man who always looked as though his skin was covered in a fine dust of flour.

"Yes, it's you as has baked the pie, isn't it?" Cissie said.

"Oh my God, I could a done without this today, I can hardly believe it. My bakery is clean as a pin. A nail yer say?"

"Yes a nail," Cissie shouted at him.

"It might be a six inch nail," my father said, sarcastically.

At once Cissie rounded on him. "It's no laughing matter, Leonard. This could do us a lot of damage. Why don't you go up see her with him?"

"I think I've had enough today, what with one thing and another; I only buried me wife this morning."

Mr Bowcock looked shocked at this. "Oh I am sorry, I didn't realise. I'll go myself and try to sort it out. It was a nail you said? Perhaps she meant a fingernail?"

"No a nail, a rusty nail," Cissie snapped.

"Oh she did say it was a rusty nail, did she," Mr. Bowcock said looking even more worried.

"Yes, and there some mouse droppings as well," Cissie said, staring angrily at him.

"Oh my God, mouse droppings! Whatever are we to do?" he said, wringing his hands.

It was becoming apparent that Mr. Bowcock was not the man to send on such a mission and somehow, I don't quite know to this day how it happened, as I had only just come into the shop and still had my best suit on after going to the funeral, but I ended up going to see Mr. and Mrs. Forshaw about the poisoned pie. When I got to their house, they refused to show me the pie, but they did show me a bent and rusty nail. They were both very agitated, but I gathered that they might be prepared to forget it for a consideration. Mrs. Forshaw kept on mentioning the Health Inspector but didn't seem in any hurry to inform him, so I suggested that they both came to the shop the next day bringing the pie with them. I said I was sure my Aunt Cissie and Mr. Bowcock between them would work out some satisfactory solution for all parties. Mr. Forshaw agreed to this but Mrs. Forshaw seemed to have some doubts and kept going on about how the nail could have killed her and she didn't want such a thing to happen to anybody else.

Next morning at about ten o'clock, Cissie sent my father to the greengrocers to fetch a big bunch of flowers with instructions to have them wrapped in fancy paper, and no sooner had the Forshaws arrived than she began to make a fuss of Mrs. Forshaw indicating that the flowers were for her. Mr. Bowcock had not yet arrived but Mr. Forshaw, who was carrying a shoebox, presumably with the pie in it, opened it and showed it to my Aunt Cissie and my father. Sure enough inside the box was a pie with a big lump bitten out of it and a number of what looked like mouse droppings rolling around in it. My Aunty Cissie's immediate concern was not only about the polluted pie, but the fact she sold it as home made. A few minutes later, Mr. Bowcock came through the front door looking paler than usual. When he saw the shoebox and realising what must be in it, his cheeks began to blow in and out. Then he indicated that he'd like to see the evidence.

When Mr. Bowcock opened the lid and peered inside, for a moment he seemed shocked by what he saw. Then he bent his head closer, and before Mr. Forshaw could stop him he lifted a piece of the pie out of the box and turning first to Cissie and then to Mrs. Forshaw he declared in a magisterial tone of voice, "Madam! this is not one of our pies and certainly was not purchased at this shop."

A strangled cry came from Mr. Forshaw, "You Liar!"

"Come on Ernest, we'd better go to the public Health Inspector where we should a gone in the first place."

"You're at liberty to go wherever you want missus, but that

pie isn't a Bowcock pie. I should know me own pies by now. I've been making 'em for thirty five years."

Mr. Bowcock had suddenly become a very different man from the nervous hand-wringing creature of the night before.

"Pies missus, I've made millions of 'em, but this isn't one. I can lay me life on that! I make steak pies. Not steak and *kidney* pies. I've never used kidney in my life. Our family has always been plagued by kidney trouble. My own mother died of it so I took against kidneys and swore I'd never use one in any pie I ever made."

As he stated this he bent down and examined the pie again, then pointed his finger at it triumphantly. "There you are. Kidney! I can see it from here."

Mr Forshaw stood staring at him with a look of bafflement on his face, but his wife wasn't defeated yet.

"I bought that pie from this shop the day before yesterday."

"Not if it's steak and kidney, yer didn't. If yer can find a steak and kidney pie in this shop I'll give yer a hundred pound. I only stock Bowcock's pies," my Aunty Cissie said, making a gesture as though to invite the Forshaws to inspect the premises.

"Why, it says in the window they're 'home made pies'. That's a lie for a start," Mrs. Forshaw stormed back at her.

"How dare you call me a liar, I wouldn't be surprised if you'd put the nail in the pie yourself. Go, go, woman. Go to the public health inspector, you haven't got a leg to stand on. Leave these premises at once." Cissie pointed to the door.

Mrs Forshaw was now fuming with rage, but her husband was looking confused and worried. "Come on Hilda."

"They're lying, both of them, can't yer see it," his wife stormed at him.

"Come on Hilda." Mr. Forshaw pulled her toward the door, but she was so angry that she turned on him.

"You make me sick, you do. You'll let anybody push you around. Let go of me arm," she shouted. But he still pulled her after him. Then as he got her outside, she pointed to the notice board in the window and shouted hysterically so everybody in the street could hear, "Home made pies, home made lies, they're liars, liars, the lot of 'em."

Her husband managed to drag her further away and Mr Bowcock turned to us all in the shop and remarked, "My word, he's got summat put up with, that man has."

"Never a dull moment," my Aunty Cissie said, lifting the bunch of flowers up. She turned to my father. "I tell you what Len, put these on Lily's grave." And that was the last we heard of the Forshaws and the polluted pie.

Chapter Nine

I have since tried to remember if this occurred before the war or just after the war was declared, but so many important life-changing things happened to me about that time, that I have got the exact timing of most of them confused. I knew that war was declared. I heard it on the wireless and I was glad. There'd been so much talk of war and the papers had been filled with nothing else for the last year, that if it hadn't been, I should have felt frustrated. I remember how excited everybody was. It seemed that the world had changed for the better overnight. There was a thrill in the streets. You could feel it when you got on a bus. It was on everybody's mind. The older generation who'd experienced the first war were troubled, but everybody else was agog with a mixture of apprehension tinged with excitement at the prospect of their lives being changed from the trap of the workaday world, or worse still, the doleday world, where a walk to the end of the street or a visit to the pictures was as far as many of them were likely to travel.

Alma could hardly contain herself. She talked of going to London and feelings between us were often very fraught. Hardly a week went past without a big row. It sometimes seemed to me that I was already involved in a war and was constantly having to retreat on all fronts. Then one day she met me as I was coming out of work. Her face was filled with trouble and as soon as I saw her standing there against the factory gate, I knew what the trouble was. She was pregnant and what was worse, she said she was four months gone. Then she raged and beat against my chest. Fate had kicked her in the teeth she cried. Just as she was thinking of getting out, she was trapped like her eldest sister who'd got three kids and was already a drudge at twenty four. The next few weeks were a nightmare; the worst time in my life.

She kept on that it was all right for me, I hadn't got to have the bloody kid and it was growing in her body. She could feel it and hated it. What were we going to do? "Don't just stand there looking bloody dumb. Oh I hate you," she'd scorp at me until I dreaded seeing her.

It was true we were both trapped by the life growing in her belly. When I was alone, I'd think of all the times before she was pregnant when I hadn't known how well off I was; times filled with laughing trivialities. I'd look at other people up and down the streets and think, why have I got all this trouble when every body else seems all right, and when I heard of men of my age getting called up, going into the army, or the navy, I'd envy them, and think what a bloody trap sex was. A lot of jiggling up and down for about five minutes and you paid for it with the best part of your life. All these thoughts went round and round in my mind every hour of the day, until I felt like a rat biting it's own tail. Alma was worse, much worse. At times she became hysterical. What were we going to do? What was I going to do? She kept on and on at me. Well out of the few avenues of possibilities that were open to us, we chose the worst. We got married. It was without doubt the biggest single mistake I ever made, and at the time I knew it was, but somehow I was hypnotised by our dilemma.

I remember as I fastened my best tie on the day we were going to the registery office, my father raged at me, "You bloody idiot, can't yer see what yer getting into?"

My sister Phoebe just smiled and asked if I knew for certain the child was mine. But none of what they said made any difference. I felt that what we were doing was inevitable. It had to be done. It was the only way the log jam could be released. There were few people at the wedding; Alma's sister Doris was there with Alma, and a youth from work called Bronco was the best man. When the deed was done, we had a drink in the smoke room of the Red Lion and then went our different ways, Alma to her mother's and me back to my father's. We hadn't been able to find anywhere to live as my father and Phoebe refused to have Alma in the house, and I refused to live at Alma's mother's because I would have had to sleep in the parlour. I should think it unlikely that any marriage had ever had such a bleak start.

My Aunty Cissie made no comment other than to make Alma come to work that night as one of the other girls had kept being sick and had gone home. Getting married had in fact separated us, and what was worse, I was glad of it. Any sexual feelings I'd had for Alma had disappeared. All I could see when I looked at her was trouble, and I felt that she hated the sight of me. This went on for months, till one day she didn't come to work. Her sister Doris came instead and told me Alma'd had a miscarriage and was in the hospital. At once I made my way to see her, but when I got there they said they'd let her go home so I hurried back to where she lived. When I got there Doris came and said Alma didn't want to see me, but would I leave the money I had been giving her each week. I left what money I had on me, and as I walked down the street, I remember I was filled with mixed emotions. In one way I was glad not to have seen her. I'd have been relieved if I'd have been told I'd never see her again. Yet there was a strange curiosity in me. As her pregnancy was well advanced, I wondered about the child, my child, that had almost made it into the world. Was it a boy or girl. There were many things I wanted to know, but was afraid of asking.

When I told my father, all he said was "You're a Lucky bugger. You've been let off the hook. Get shut of her."

Phoebe's reaction was different. She'd always suggested that the child might not be mine, but now she seemed genuinely sorry for what had happened. As usual she was in a load of trouble herself with someone she'd given the heave-ho to, who kept pestering her to such an extent she'd reported him to the police.

My Aunty Cissie's reaction was to clench her jaw and shake her head as though she'd never heard of such terrible goings on, but all she was really concerned about was whether she'd have to get another girl or not. "It puts me in a funny position doesn't it? I don't know where I am, I should never a started her. They make me sick these wenches do. There's always summat up with 'em. The are up and down three parts naked and then they wonder why they get in trouble."

Not long after this, I decided to join up. I'd been thinking about it for some time and had on a number of occasions made up my mind the night before to join up next day, but when the light of morning came, I'd thought better of it. Now I felt I needed a complete change. There were many young men I knew who were in the forces and when they came home on leave dressed in their uniforms, filled with stories of other places, it made me restless. So one day I made my way to the recruiting office just to make enquiries. I wasn't going to commit myself. Then as I entered the building, something happened which to this day I can't quite understand, except that it is typical of me, as many time in my life, when I've started out to buy something, and entered a shop with no doubt as to what I wanted, I've come out with something completely different. So on the day I entered the recruiting office, my intention was clear. I wanted to join His Majesty's forces and yet, when I came out of the building I'd signed my name to become a Bevin Boy in one of the local pits. I think it was telling them my father had worked in the pit that decided it. They seemed to want colliers more than soldiers that day, and must have thought that pit work ran in the family and the pit was the place for me. A week later, I received a postcard instructing me to report to a training pit in Cannock in the south of the county.

When my father found out what I'd done, he roared with laughing. "You'll never stick it," he prophesied. "I can just see you, first rope down on Monday morning, scrawling about in a two foot seam."

But for all his derisive laughter, I sensed that he was pleased, as although he'd left the pit many years, he always reckoned "Once a pit man, always a pit man," and no talk pleased him more than pit talk. If ever an old collier came into the chip shop, they'd start drawing coal at once and one occasion when Herbert Pepper had been there and made some sarcastic remark about the roof falling in, my father had turned viciously and said, "Bollocks" to him. Another reason that may have helped me choose the pit rather than the army was the money was better and although me and Alma didn't live together and certainly didn't sleep together, we were nevertheless married. As she was legally my wife, I was obliged to support her and Alma always had her hand out.

Whenever she saw me she'd quite brazenly say, "Money! Money! Money!" laughing at me as she said it, as though I was a fool. This enraged my father who said he'd go to jail before he'd pay her a halfpenny. I could only hope she'd get another fella soon and marry him to let me off the hook.

"Get another fella!" Our Phoebe laughed aloud when I said it. "Get another fella! Why half the Lancashire Fusileers have been through their parlour. The lot of 'em are on the game. Her mother's, hawking it about the town like a wench of sixteen, six inch heels, short skirt, the lot, and you're helping keep her. You must be crackers."

It was true the Lancashire Fusileers were stationed in a mill near the town. There were also Dutch Troops from Queen Whilhelmina's bodyguard stationed there as well and the town pubs were always filled with soldiers, young part time prostitutes and old full time whores, and there were rumours that the Yanks were coming over.

Phoebe was very excited about this. "It'll make a change from the lot stationed round here. They're bloody hopeless; they're worse than the local lads. None of 'em have got any money for a start. One stupid kid, he was only about nineteen, asked me ter marry him and go live in Accrington. I'd only been out with him once. I told I'd rather live down a grid. Oh, but the Yanks; they'll be perfect, I can't wait. Have you seen their uniforms? They're better than our officers. There's summat about 'em, just like you've seen on the pictures."

She then swooned off into:

"I can't give you anything but love baby.
That's the only thing I've got, plenty of, baby.
Dream awhile, scheme awhile,
You're sure to find

Happiness and I guess,
All the things
You've always pined for."
When I heard her sing this, I understood how deep the need
was for America in a place like this where most people's lives
were dull. Monday to Friday, God send Sunday, chained to bleak
economic rocks for a lifetime with no hope of escape. There
seemed to be glamour in everything American. Even the place
names had a music in them. Most states, and most big cities had
songs written about the. "Home in Pasadena" sounded perfect,
whereas, "Home in Chell Heath" or "Brindley Ford" sounded
silly. I myself was always deeply affected by the images of
America. When I think back to the war, what I remember most
clearly are the great escapist musicals made in Hollywood at that
time, in which glamorous young women like Alice Fay, Betty
Grable, Gloria de Haven and above all, Rita Hayworth, danced
and fell in love with impossibly handsome young men in places
like Rio de Janairo, Los Angeles or Honolulu. Places a long, long
way away from the chip shop and the pit.

Sometimes when I was on the day shift in one of the first
cages down on a wet Monday morning, with my stomach
rumbling and a slight headache, I'd think of someone like Rita
Hayworth, and the brutal contrast between what I imagined life
could be, and what it really was, caused my spirits to drop as fast
as the cage. And yet, from what I could see, most of the other
colliers in the cage were not troubled by romantic thoughts of
this kind. They mostly had troubles of a more immediate and
sensual nature which they complained about in filthy language.
All my life, in the streets I had been reared in, I'd heard filthy
language, but the first day I was down the pit, it was as though
I'd never heard it before. Many men who hardly swore when they
were at home, decent family men, used a stream of sexual filth to
express themselves.

I was fortunate that the overman I had to follow when I first
started was a strong methodist, Mr. Jonah Simcock, a solid,
square man, much respected in the pit. "Take no notice of this
lot, lad. They're all heathens. They'll come to no good. If they put
on thee, stand up to 'em," he said to me the first time I met him.
But I knew many of the men, and they knew my family, and this
helped me settle down to the daily grind of pit life for I felt that I
had a right to be in this pit as many of both sides of my family
had worked there. I had not been working there long before there
was an accident. A man got crushed by pit tubs. I did not see it
happen, but when I came up the pit I had occasion to go into the

lamp house and saw his body under a white sheet.

"He's gone dead," a little fat man standing against the body said. "Broke his back. There was nowt we could do. They 'anna told his missus yet. As soon as I saw him I knew he was a gonner. He comes from down against the Cemetery. There's one thing, he wunner have far go."

I was shocked by the offhand way the man spoke, but as I stood by the lamp house door about to go out into the sunshine, he seemed to sense what I was thinking and said sadly. "He'll never see the sun again, the poor bugger wunna."

As I walked home toward the town, everything I usually passed without a glance looked beautiful.

Although I was working in the pit and earning reasonable money when I was on the day shift, I still helped out at the chip shop. This helped with what I gave Alma each week. The payment infuriated my father who couldn't contain himself about it. Each week when I paid, he'd get himself worked up into a rage at me.

"By God, her saw you coming Alma did. Her's made you pay for yer bit a leg over. I wouldn't give her a halfpenny. I'd go jail first. Couldn't yer see what her was after? What the hell you had to marry her for? He stormed at me in this fashion again and again. It was a constant source of rows between us. I'd shout at him that it was none of his business, but it made no difference.

Alma by now was up and down the pubs with her sister and I heard tell of her with soldiers, and hoped against hope that she'd meet somebody and want to get married again. This brought another bitter storm from my father.

"Why should her get married to anybody? Her's got one silly bugger keeping her already. No, her's got more bloody sense, Alma has. Her can have a good time and know thee't pay the bill."

At this time he was also much concerned about Phoebe who'd gone to work in an armaments factory in Birmingham with her friend Ivy and although she'd promised to write to him, she hardly ever did, and I knew she was continually on his mind. He was now about fifty years of age and beginning to show it. I often caught him looking at himself in the mirror in such a way that I could tell he was becoming aware of his aging. We hardly ever had much conversation together and when we did, it was mainly about the chip shop, which had gradually become his life. He argued with Cissie as though he was a part owner instead of just an ill-paid lackey lad, and when Herbert Pepper tried to interest her in buying an old van and turning it into a mobile chip shop for him and his son Norbert to sell fish and chips on the housing estates on the perimeter of the town, there was a row between them.

"I've never heard of anything so daft in me life. I'm surprised at you Cissie," he said angrily.

"What's so daft about it?" Herbert asked indignantly. "It 'erd made a fortune. Folks can't afford to come to the town every night."

"A fire in the back, why yer daft bugger, it'erd blow up," my father ridiculed the idea.

"Blow up me foot. I tell yer it 'erd work," Herbert argued and Cissie looked as though she was becoming convinced. But whenever he started to mention what it would cost to set it up, she drew back.

Then one day he came hurrying into the shop and said he'd seen a van that would be perfect for the job and it wouldn't want much doing to convert it. He'd worked out what it would cost to fit it out. He'd even worked out what the profits would be. It all sounded very promising, and Cissie was seriously considering it, when not long after, she heard one of the girls, who did a bit of part time work for her, shriek with laughing from the back room. It was the kind of laugh that indicated something was going on that shouldn't be. Cissie went to investigate and was appalled by what she saw. Norbert who was supposed to be cleaning potatoes, had found a big one and had fashioned it into the shape of a penis and was holding it between his legs. The girl was standing there tittering at him.

For a second, Cissie was so shocked that she stood still. Then she rushed at him flailing and screaming, "Get out! get out! You dirty pig." Some of her blows struck him and he put his arms up to protect his head, but there was no stopping her wrath. She was disgusted and infuriated by what she'd seen. "Get out, get out of my shop!" she shouted and as Norbert retreated to the back door, he attempted to say something but there was no defence and he knew it, so he rushed down the yard and disappeared leaving the girl trembling with fear and Cissie breathless and coughing.

Later that day Herbert hurried to the shop and attempted to explain his son's action. "It was only a lad's trick Cissie, a lad's trick!"

She spat out, "Not a lad I want in this shop, Herbert. he must never put his foot in here again the filthy beast."

"Hold on Cissie," Herbert began to remonstrate.

"D'yer hear what I say. He must never put his foot in this

shop again and that's the end of it as far as I'm concerned," Cissie shouted.

Herbert had never seen her this angry before and thought better of trying to argue with her, hoping that in a few days when she'd calmed down he'd bring up the subject of the van again. But when he did, she turned on him furiously.

"I've told yer, Herbert, he's finished here Norbert has, and don't bring the subject up again."

By now she had seen through all Herbert's little tricks, but somehow liked having him around, and it must have been the same with him, for at times she was as ill-tempered with him as she was with my father. She thought him a fool with money because he backed horses and put money on the football pools.

"A man of his age., You'd think he'd got more sense." She even ridiculed his banding. "He's like a big soft kid with that trumpet. He's a fool, Herbert is. He'll never amount to anything," she'd say dismissively if his name came up.

The shop was now flourishing as the rationing in the war years was good for the chip business. Cissie always managed to get potatoes and fat, even if at times she had to pay over the odds for it. She had no scruples about using the black market. Money was money, and money was the morality she understood. Sentiments of a national and patriotic kind didn't exist for her. She made no account of things beyond her immediate world and it was more than enough to sustain her. Although one day was much like another, one week like another, one year like another, she never seemed bored.

Her world was behind the counter from early morning till late at night an she didn't seem to need fresh air; indeed when she went outside it started her coughing. The warm chip smelling fug in the shop suited her bronchial lungs and it seemed to me that she had been born to live and work in the shop. It was her creation and she was in the very centre of it. In the mornings she often looked so haggard and ill you'd think she was on the point of collapse. At these times she'd take a pinch of snuff to get her brain going and by the time my father arrived and one or other of the girls she employed, she'd have pulled herself together and would start rasping out orders. Then they'd open the shop door at about eleven.

The first fry was at twelve, ready for the stream of factory workers who came for enormous orders which they'd carry away in vertical piles of parcels back to the factory bench where they and their friends worked. This went on for about three quarters of an hour and was the time of most concentrated effort in the day, after which there'd be a short period of relative quiet when they'd all have a cup of tea and get their breath back. As a rule there'd be a steady trade during the afternoon. The shop now sold all sorts of food; tripe, chicklings, hodge, cow heel, a great variety of pies and sausage rolls and cups of tea and bread and butter with meals in the dining room.

After three o'clock each day there'd be a number of men, and occasionally women, who'd been drinking till the pubs closed and wanted somewhere to sit till they opened again at six o'clock. There was occasional trouble with some of these, but the fear of being blacklisted made most of them behave themselves. The dining room had become a waiting room for the boozers of the town, and Cissie used to say she'd make a fortune if she could get a licence to sell drink. There were also a number of social misfits, human curiosities who frequented the reading room and used the chip shop every day.

A man named Elijah Price, was a religious maniac who used to stand on the top of the gentlemen's lavatory preaching to whoever would listen to him, although he was so far gone in his private mania that he would preach if there was nobody listening. His message to the world was mostly about sin and redemption, but the sin part came over most vividly. He was a short squat man with some impediment in his mouth which caused his front two top teeth to protrude outside his lips and his head was at such an angle on his neck that the inside of his nostrils were always visible. He always wore the same dark clothes which looked as though he'd slept in them for year — a dark homburg hat and a raincoat with, strangely, a bit of string knotted in a noose hanging down a few inches from the collar at the back. Whether he had fixed this on himself or whether somebody else had fastened it on without him noticing I could not tell, but somehow it perfectly summed up this malevolent, and at the same time comic, personality.

He spent most of his days in the municipal reading room muttering to himself, and occasionally going outside to empty a jam jar into the grid. I think this jar contained urine, and that he must have relieved himself in it concealed under his raincoat. There had been a number of complaints about him from the other men that used the place. One said he stank like an otter. Another, a man as twisted as himself, had threatened to stab him with a knife. The caretaker of the place, Mr. Gutteridge, had fetched the Police, but it had blown over. Such things had no effect of Elijah, as he was used to taunts and abuse from louts when he preached. When this happened, he'd put his hands

Elijah Price

together and pray for the sinners, sometimes even getting down on his hands and knees to do it. He usually came into the chip shop in late afternoon. Often he had done his preaching and bought a few pennies worth of chips and a cup of tea. He would sit in the dining room till after six o'clock when he'd go back to the hostel where he lived.

Sometimes he'd begin to preach or sing hymns in the shop.

"In my heart there rings a melody,
Rings a melody, rings a melody,
In my heart there rings a melody,
Rings a melody of love"

This was one he used to pipe up with if he was in a good mood. But if his face was red and the veins at the side of his forehead were sticking out, it would be sin and hell fire he'd rant on about. Cissie told him on a number of occasions that if he didn't stop upsetting the other customers, she'd bar him out. But it made no difference.

One day he came to the shop and began banging on the counter with a tin salt cellar shouting that the churches were all telling lies, and that the parsons were all fornicators. "Souls! They're always preaching about souls; they've got no souls. Poverty and humility, they're the Christian virtues. Tell the parsons that and they don't want to hear you. I have lived on bread and carrot! Have they? No, they live on the fat of the land. If I tell you a lie may the Lord strike me dead this minute."

He was banging the salt cellar down on the counter as he said this and my Aunt Cissie cut in, "Not in here Elijah, don't drop dead in here duck."

"Have no fear Miss Salt, I have much work to do before I meet my Maker. There is a lie I have to expose," he said, looking about him suspiciously.

"And what's that Elijah?" Cissie said trying to humour him.

A twisted smile crossed his face and he bent forward toward her. "It's about Jesus Christ being the Son of God."

"Oh, what about it?" she said.

"Jesus Christ was not the Son of God. His father was an Italian Legionnaire."

Cissie looked astounded. "An Italian Legionnaire," she repeated the words looking shocked.

"An Eye talion Legionnaire. The truth came to me as I slept. It was a revelation. Oh, how I wish it were not so, but I must tell the people. That's my task."

"They'll lock you up you daft devil," my father interjected.

Elijah turned and glared at him. "Oh yes, they'll shackle me to the walls. They'll hate me because I tell the truth. Gutteridge hates me. They will all hate me."

"Gutteridge, who's he?" my father asked.

"An evil man who works in the Library. He's tried to have me banned out, but I'll have him sacked then *he'll* be banned out. Yer know what he does?"

"I've no idea," my father said, smiling in a patronising way.

"He takes a parcel home every day from the Library. Yer know what's in it?"

"The crafty devil," my father laughed.

"He's pinching soap and soap powder. Every day he takes it. He's bought a bungalow out 'er what he's pinched from that Library. But I'm going to report him, then we'll see who gets banned out."

"What's soap got ter do with the Italian Legionnaires. You've gone off the subject," Cissie said.

"Oh no I haven't; I know what I know and you don't know," he said glaring at my father.

"Yer right there duck, he only thinks he does," Cissie interjected.

Elijah then seemed confused, and started feeling in his pockets to see what coins he had and when he'd carefully counted them he must have decided he hadn't enough, for he lifted his homburg and turning toward the door a mad smile came over his face.

"I think I'll go back to the hostel for have me tea. I'm very satisfied there yer know and me mother is as well."

"Yer mother's been dead years man," Cissie said looking annoyed.

For a second Elijah thought about this; then the smile left his face, "Oh yes, her says we've all got have a bath every week now."

"Oh that'll do you good. It'll freshen yer up a bit," my father said laughingly.

Elijah's face sank at this and he said sullenly, "I don't want one and I'm not having one."

"Don't take any notice of him duck, he's only having yer on," Cissie said.

Then Elijah got a piece of dirty rag out of his coat pocket, wiped his eyes and face with it and without saying anything more, he stalked off.

"An Italian Legionnaire eh. I've never heard a that before. I wonder where he's got that one from. It'll come as a big surprise to a lot 'er folks that one will," my father said as he bent down to turn the gas up.

"You shouldn't torment him, he can't help how he is. I sometimes feel I'm going funny myself," Cissie said.

"I've noticed," my father muttered as he straightened up. Then he groaned and felt at his back which had recently been giving him a lot of discomfort. "My back's giving me some humpy lately. It's old age I reckon, and my joints are definitely beginning to stiffen up."

My Aunty Cissie was also troubled by rheumatism and her fingers were misshapen by it, But she never complained of any physical ache or pain, and had no time for anybody with anything that interfered with the working of the chip shop. She didn't want to hear about it. It was as though to her the buying and eating of chips was what humanity had come into existence for. She could conceive of no higher calling than to make money out of the marriage of hot fat and potato.

Chapter Ten

Very occasionally Cissie would take some interest in the doings of the world outside her shop. One such was when Mrs. Potts, Mrs. Adeline Potts to give her her full name, was involved in a near tragedy. Mrs. Potts you may remember, was famous in the town for completely occupying a small snug at the Star public house for as long as most people could remember. A toby jug of a woman, heavy and squat as a frog, with a mouth that seemed to stretch all across her face. She had seen publicans come and go and was familiar with all the primal functions of life, such as the breaking of the water, birth, rashes on babies arses, death in all it's various manifestations, and the working or non working of bowels. All these were regularly the subject of her conversation as she sucked her Guinness and chommelled her sandwiches. But she and Elijah Price were part of a life that was rapidly disappearing. They were the last outcrop of my grandfather's world, when gaslight, horse muck and straw were a part of everyday life.

My Aunty Cissie was a part of that world as well, and each of them was sustained by such powerful private appetites, that the life force was still very strong in them. In Elijah's case it was madness, in Cissie's her money and in Mrs. Potts it was her simple pleasures which never failed her. She must in her time have eaten herds of pigs and certainly drunk enough Guinness to float a boat as she sat in the snug each day warming herself against a small stove.

Another woman of the same generation always came and sat with her. Lottie Tippen was not such a dominant character. She always seemed frozen and had a hen-like appearance enhanced by a dirty piece of fur she always wore round her neck. She was very similar to her friend Mrs. Potts in her liking for Guinness, but instead of roast pork sandwiches, her preference was for Chicklings which she bought from the chip shop, and it was from her pale and cracked lips that we heard the details of the near tragedy that had befallen both of them.

"It was as though it had got ter happen, but the Lord spared us, thank God."

Her telling of the tale was so fragmented by her constant thanking God for sparing them, that I will cut a long story short. It seems that Mrs. Potts left her home as usual to attend the Star public house at morning opening time, and on the way she met Lottie coming from the doctors. It came on raining so they decided to call in a public house called the Royal Exchange,

Mrs. Potts

otherwise known as the Jig Post. Mrs. Potts hadn't been there for twenty years, but as it was raining hard they both went in ordered Guinness, and sat down in the smoke room waiting for the rain to subside.

The room was empty and dark the only light coming from a skylight above. They sipped their Guinness and made the best of it hoping that the rain would soon go off. Then just as Mrs. Potts was lifting her glass, they heard a slight rumbling, followed by a creaking sound, the room went darker and there was a terrible explosion. A split second later they were covered in broken glass, broken brick and soot. Lottie screamed and Mrs Potts choked. They thought that a German bomb must have dropped on them. The publican, a wheezy little fat man ran to the back door, then back down the passage like a trapped animal.

What had happened they found, was that the wind had blown a chimney pot down, and it had fallen through the skylight directly above where Mrs. Potts and Lottie were sitting. The shock was so great that Lottie collapsed and had to be given brandy. Mrs. Potts, who was made of much sterner stuff, found the top of her Guinness was covered in soot, and demanded another one from the publican. When he refused she became furious and threatened to report him to the brewery. After some further altercation he gave in and poured her another.

The news of this accident spread quickly through the pubs and most boozers expressed the opinion that sitting in a pub with a Guinness in yer hand was a good way to go.

A few weeks later, Mrs. Potts, hearing her friend Lottie speak of the wonders of the dining room, decided to have a look for herself. She had never stepped in the chip shop before as she had no appetite for chips. Having been reared on them as a child and having brought her own family up on them as a young woman, she often said she'd seen enough of chip pans and chips to last her a lifetime and anyway roast pork suited her much better. Notwithstanding this, one day as she left the snug in the Star, instead of making her way home, she turned down the Waterloo Road, and with her friend Lottie at her side, made her way steadily to the chip shop. For a moment, she stood outside, taking in a general view of the place, then stepping inside she greeted my Aunt Cissie.

"Hello Cissie duck, I've come for see yer at last. I've heard so much about this shop."

The familiarity with which she greeted my Aunt Cissie can be understood by the fact that they were both women of strong character, and each in her own way, in their very different spheres were well known in the town. They had both by dint of their personalities made their mark, and no doubt would be spoken about years after they were dead. It is not given to many women of the working class to achieve such distinction.,

"I've come for see this 'ere dining room Cissie, I've heard such a lot about it from Lottie. Her's allus going on about it."

"It's upstairs," Lottie chipped in.

"Go on up," Cissie said.

"I've a job get upstairs these day. I've had me bed down in the parlour for years," Mrs. Potts complained.

"Well that's where it is duck," Cissie said wiping the counter in front of her.

"Come on then Lottie," said Mrs. Potts. "Stand behind me as I go up and give me a push if I stop."

She moved her great bulk toward the staircase and slowly began to mount the stairs with Lottie behind her, and after some groaning and complaining they reached the top, while Cissie and my father stood listening below.

"My God, we are honoured! Her's never been in this shop before not while I've been here. Her's a nosy old bugger," my father said.

"I don't suppose her's come for anything," Cissie smiled knowingly, lifting a salt cellar and wiping it. "Her's just come for a look."

My father laughed. Then a few minutes later, there was a noise from the top of the stairs.

"Hold on ter me arm Lottie," Mrs. Potts could be heard saying, as in a moment or two, after much heaving and groaning, she appeared at the top coming down sideways.

"There's no labatry, no labatry," she gasped accusingly.

"Oh, there is, but it's out of order. Yer should see the state it was in. They'd broken the chain off and cracked the cistern. I had to lock it up on Sunday. It turns yer sick ter see it."

"There *is* a labatry up there then?" said Mrs. Potts looking.

"Oh yes, it's at the far end, but it's out 'er bound. They are not human beings as use this place, they're animals, only animals are better than the lot as use this place. Yer should see the mess they leave," Cissie said. But Mrs. Potts didn't seem to hear.

"I thought you'd got have a labatry if you've got a dining room," she went on.

"I tell you, we've got one, but it's out of order," Cissie repeated impatiently.

"It's the same as a pub; you couldn't have a pub without a

labatry. That's why I allus use the Star. From where I sit in the snug, it's only a step or two ter the ladies, in't it Lottie?" Lottie who was partly outside the shop, nodded in support. "Her suffers bad in that direction don't you duck," Mrs. Potts went on.

"I'm up and down all night. Once I start it's all over. No sooner I've sat meself down than I'm there again," Lottie said adjusting the fur collar of her coat.

"Come on then, we'll go. Any road Cissie, I'm very glad for see yer doing so well, duck. You must a worked hard for get all this, for you'd nothing start with, had yer? I allus say 'good luck' ter anybody as makes their way in the world," Mrs. Potts went on as she was about to step outside.

"I'll have the red carpet out when yer call again," my father said.

This remark seemed to confuse Mrs. Potts.

"Red carpet? Yer dunna have red carpet down do yer?" she asked wonderingly.

"Take no notice of him, it's only his daft," Cissie said.

"I thought you'd never put carpet down in a chip shop, but you never know these days. Folks do funny things. There's no accounting for 'em. Just think Cissie; there was nothing 'er this when we were wenches, was there?" She indicated toward the main road. "Well ta ra then duck, I'll call again, one 'er these days.

Lottie smiled and waved through the shop window as they both made their way back up the road toward the traffic lights.

"Well, well, wonders never cease. We have been honoured; Lady Muck's been on a guided tour," my father said. "You think her was somebody. Her's nowt but an old soak."

Cissie muttered a reply to this but her mind was already on other things, and she started to examine the window thinking about how to make it more attractive. She often broke off conversations in this way as though she didn't consider the matter worth discussion, and regularly accused my father of listening to tittle tattle, even if he mentioned the way the war was going. She'd either try to bring the conversation back to the chip shop or ignore it altogether.

Herbert Pepper now hardly ever came to the shop, which pleased my father, but when Cissie decided to have some decorating done at her house, she sent for him as she knew he'd do it cheaper than a proper painter and decorator. My father offered to do it himself, but he was very rough and slapdash and Herbert, while not being an expert, was nevertheless a neat worker. Cissie was very particular, especially about paper hanging. Once, when my father had done some papering for her she said he hadn't matched the patterns. He'd protested that there wasn't any patterns, only millions of coloured dots. She said there was a pattern in the dots, and there'd been a row between them. So that Herbert Pepper was chosen to do the decorating and as she was at the shop six days a week from morning till night, she gave him the house key and let him get on with it. This seems to me now to have been amazing, as she had a lot of money hidden in the house; but on reflection I realise it wasn't so surprising. She was very suspicious about people and trusted no one, yet I can remember how she regularly sent one of the girls who worked for her to go and do a bit of cleaning.

Anyway, as far as Herbert Pepper and the decorating went, she seemed to have no qualms. Everything went very well and when she got home at night she was surprised at how much he'd done, that is until she found a fag packet. She knew that Herbert didn't smoke so she was suspicious, and next day when she put the matter to him he was forced to admit that he'd let Norbert help him.

"I thought I told you Herbert, that I didn't want that young man in this shop anymore."

"He hasn't been in this shop has he?" Herbert said defiantly.

"No he hasn't, he's been in my house, which is worse. Now listen ter me, Herbert Pepper. I don't want him anywhere near any 'er my property."

"He was only scraping paper off," Herbert protested. But for all his protests, Cissie would not have Norbert at any price. If she took against somebody, it was final. I myself at this time was not in her good books as I began to suit my own conveniences and not hers. I was now trying to get out of the pit on medical grounds as I was finding the weekly grind of shift work and the constant mauling was wearing me down. I was also beginning to suffer from a touch of bronchitis and it troubled me to see that my phlegm was black with coal dust when I spit.

Every night at this time, the pubs of the town were filled with Yanks who were billeted in factory buildings in the next town. I got to know a few of them, and the ease with which they spent money, struck me painfully as I often had to count my pennies for my weekly payment to Alma which took a big bite out of my wages. Everything the Yanks did or had was more stylish and richer than anybody hereabout could even dream of. The local men who used the pubs with their few woodbines and their drab clothes were a poverty stricken lot compared to them. The way they talked, the way they walked, the colour of their skin, the cigars they smoked, had an elegance that reminded me of the world in the films I'd seen. It was not only the clothes and the money either, it was something else. There was a democracy about them. They were different with their officers. There didn't seem to be any class system in their army, where ours was riddled with it. In fact I could never remember seeing a British Officer in any of the town pubs I used.

The contrast between my life down the pit, with my black spit and the bleak prospect before me and the way they were disturbed me greatly, and thoughts of emigrating came to my mind. But when I spoke to my father about it, he said patriotically, "England is the finest country in the world; it's all flash America is."

I said I could do with a bit of flash so he accused me of seeing too many films and not facing reality. When I replied that the reality I was facing had brought me to such an opinion, he flew off the handle and despaired of my whole generation, who according to him, had always had it soft, and it was that as was responsible for how our Phoebe behaved. He contrasted her with my Aunt Cissie who had amounted to something. At this I said that Cissie was a scrawmer who only loved money and had no human feelings. This enraged him because he knew it was true, and had on occasion suggested as much himself. I should be trying to keep in with Cissie as she was getting on and who else would she leave her money to? It wasn't himself he was thinking about, it was me, but I was such a bloody idiot I couldn't see it.

"You have to hold a candle to the devil," he kept on preaching to me. I should be helping the chip shop instead of hanging round the pubs listening to soft Yanks who had more money than sense. I'd always had my own pig headed way and where had it got me? If I'd have listened to him I'd a never got a bloody whore round my neck who was bleeding me white. He groaned when he said this and I inwardly groaned myself at the impossibility of ever making him understand how I felt. I knew that the pain of hardly ever hearing from Phoebe was a constant source of unhappiness to him and made him fiercely denounce all the young girls who hung around after the youths.

"This place is full of scum; they're nothing but tarts all the lot of 'em and some of 'em are still at school. Old England eh! Home of the brave Britons who never never shall be slaves. No they'll all be whores instead." He laughed bitterly. "It's all eyewash, all propaganda, they're cracking a bloody good nut some buggers are out 'er this lot. I've seen it before, but the working class are bloody daft, or most of 'em are."

He often went on in this way but I never heard him express any direct political opinions. He usually started off by castigating the working class for only wanting to get their noses in a pint pot. Then he'd end up by suggesting there were all sorts of conspiracies against them. But on most occasions, I was the whipping boy, the target for his sarcasms.

"By God, her saw you coming, that bitch did. I'll bet her got the best biscuits out fer yer and put a fire in the parlour, and you, yer silly bugger, walked right into it with yer eyes wide open and all fer a bit of jiggling up and down."

He was often very funny in the comments he made but at the time I usually didn't feel like laughing. Then a miracle happened.

Alma wrote to me asking for a divorce as she was going to marry a G.I. named Danny Casperovitch. When my father heard about this, his emotions were confused between a genuine relief for me and a desire to make the most of the situation sarcastically.

"You are a lucky bugger. What d'yer say his name is, Danny Casperovitch? He's either a pole or a Jew or an Eyetie. Dare to be a Daniel, eh?" he laughed. "He must be bloody crackers. I heard tell her mother and her sister were hawking their mutton up and down in the Majestic last Saturday night. Her mother must be sixty if her's a day. I'll bet her's older than me. Yer know what her reminds me of? One of them insects I was reading about. When the male has fertilised the female, her eats him. Serve the daft bugger right. He must a died happy."

He would often pick up pieces of miscellaneous information from the magazine Tit-Bits which he took every week and would usually manage to introduce them into his conversation. I was often surprised by his grasp of matter I didn't think he could possibly understand. The papers were full of the hydrogen bomb in those days and he knew the names of physicists like Oppenheimer and Tzillard, and when Herbert Pepper called at the shop he'd speak on such matters authoritively. I even heard him mention Einstein and the theory of relativity once, but when Herbert looked puzzled and wanted to know more, he was soon in deep water.

"I don't mind admitting it, Herbert, but I don't understand it, and neither does anybody else round here. But I do know who Einstein is, which is a damn sight more than anybody else as comes into this chip shop does. I often think Herbert, that my brain could a stood a lot more education."

Herbert looked as though he doubted this. "It's the same

with me and music," he said thoughtfully.

"Oh no it isn't, music's different, it's more of a gift. I mean real brain work, not blowing a bloody trumpet," my father replied irritably.

A flash of anger crossed Herbert's face, "What's most important, giving people pleasure or blowing them up? What's the use of bombs? I know which I'd rather have."

"Oh we know which you'd rather have Herbert — trumpets! Oh, that's what's up with this country, Herbert. Too many trumpets and not enough real brainwork."

They often argued bitterly but there was no jealousy. My father no longer thought that Herbert was after Cissie's money, or if he thought it, he realised he had no chance of being successful. She now regarded Herbert as an amiable fool, useful for doing odd jobs, cheap about the house. She joked about him blowing his own trumpet and Norberts name was never mentioned. Herbert, for his part, had got so used to coming to the chip shop that it had become a second home for him; a place where there was a lot of chitchat going on.

After the atom bomb had been dropped on Japan and the war was coming to it's end, all I clearly remember of Victory was that Cissie refused absolutely to buy a Union Jack, and we had to decorate the shop with a number of carrier bags, with Union Jacks printed on the front, hanging on a string across the big window. I was now divorced thank God, and I was told Alma had gone to America as a GI bride.

Occasionally we got a letter from Phoebe. In one of them she said she was engaged to a man who'd got his own business, but there was no mention of it in the next letter. My father hardly ever spoke about her but I knew she was always on his mind.

"We've all got our worries to bear," he'd say philosophically if anybody mentioned troubles of any kind. If Cissie heard him in this mood she'd pooh pooh the idea that he or anybody else knew what trouble was compared to her.

"You want have the worry of running this place," she'd say.

"What worries have you got," my father would retort.

"You don't know; nobody knows; my head's just like a basketfull of adders when I put it on the pillow at night. The thoughts keep going round and round as fast as a spinning top."

"It's counting the takings as does that," my father would usually reply and this would immediately put her on the defensive.

"Whatever I've got, I've worked for Leonard. You've all had the same chance as me."

"There's plenty as have worked as hard as you Cissie, some harder and got nowt for it. It's luck you've had. I remember my father saying so once."

Cissie turned on him, "I've worked with me brains as well. Nobody knows the worry I've had."

"It's luck I tell you," my father rejoined. "There's winners and there's losers. Suppose everybody had done what you've done; there'd be bloody thousands of chip shops in this town. Yer wouldna like that would yer?"

I remember Cissie had looked a bit confused at this and the argument had petered out. Sometimes I felt that she got at my father through the way I was living. I nightly attended four or five pubs in the town, and had no ambition beyond being able to continue in this way. If for some reason I couldn't go on my usual round, having a pint in one then moving to another, I'd feel frustrated and unhappy. Even the pull of going to the pictures was becoming less. I was beginning to appreciate and enjoy the richness of the pub life. I knew all the characters and was known by them. I was the friend of a number of the big boozers, the popes of the tap rooms, the mafiosi of drink and I very rarely put my head in the chip shop. This didn't trouble my Aunty Cissie as much as it did my father, who as usual called me a fool for not keeping in with her; but after a day's work, the last thing I wanted was to carry trays of fish and chips up the stairs to the dining room.

What I enjoyed was being among the great bustle of the town at night and I often felt the attraction of certain females. At times it was so strong that I'd yearn for one or another of them, but fortunately I was curious in this matter. If I was attracted to a decent woman, a person I could respect and possibly fall in love with, I hardly ever fancied her sexually. The women that excited me physically were almost always sluts who I had no respect for. The more face paint, the shorter the skirt, the more I lusted after them, but even these were not attractive enough for me to give up a night in the pubs. I had to attend a bar each night. They were like altars to me. The sight of the spirit bottles, the optics and all the glittering bits and pieces comforted me greatly. Sitting or standing at a bar having a drink was where I was happiest. Not that I had a lot of drink. To hear my father go on about me, anybody would have thought I was an alcoholic. But it wasn't true. I used to have four pints a night, which among drinking men is nothing. I never went into pubs during the day, and I usually didn't go out at night till after nine o'clock and was home by about half past ten. My father never got in till after twelve, as when they closed the shop he'd go to the night safe at the bank with Cissie, then walk her home. I would usually be in bed by the time he got in, but still he used to upbraid me for my drinking.

It was one such night he woke me up in a very agitated state. It turned out that a person had been in the shop who said she'd seen our Phoebe in Woolworth's that day. She was sure it was her. My father was beside himself, as he'd not heard from her for more than a month and couldn't understand it.

"Her said her was sure it was Phoebe. Her'd stood just behind her. What the hell's her up to now." He sighed heavily. He sat on the side of my bed, his face taut with worry. I didn't know what to say. I was as surprised as he was. I knew what a devil Phoebe was, but I also knew she had real affection for her father and couldn't understand it.

"Surely to God she'd come home first if she'd come back," I reasoned.

"I feel sure it was her. This woman knew her. You'd a thought her'd a written to let us know. I wonder what sort of a bloody mess her's got herself in now? Her'll be up and down with some man I'll bet," he said despairingly.

I had recently been thinking that perhaps I was the same as Phoebe. She'd always seemed to prefer the company of men of bad character, flashy fly boys, curly haired tattooed louts, and I wondered if my liking for sluttish women was the same thing the other way round. But I couldn't understand her not letting us know she was back in the district, and for the next few days my father was beside himself with worry. Then one morning as the days work was just beginning in the chip shop and my father was bending down attending to the chip frying, Phoebe came quietly into the shop and stood by the counter.

"A fish and sixpennerth please," she said.

For a second my father stiffened. Then he reared up. "Where the hell have you been?" he blurted out. Before she could answer, he began to upbraid her. "Why didn't you come home, I've been worried sick. You know where your home is don't you? How long have yer been back?"

"I've only just come back. Give me a chance man," she said, flushing up.

"Oh no yer haven't, don't tell lies Phoebe. Yer were seen in Woolworth's days ago," he said, his voice filled with pain.

"Oh so yer've had yer spies out already have yer. I thought I should have to have this," she retorted angrily.

"Well what do yer expect? I've never heard a word from yer

for months, then yer turn up out of the blue and don't even come home. What do yer expect me ter think?"

"I don't care what you think, I've come for see yer now, haven't I," she snapped.

"Oh Phoebe, Phoebe, why do yer do this to me," he cried.

"Do what? I've done nothing." A flash of anger crossed her face as she said this. "Now look here, I am not, repeat not, going to be your little girl goody bloody two shoes. It isn't me, never was, and never will be. I'm me, I like being me or some of it."

"God only knows what we did wrong when we were bring you two up. Yer both selfish and pig-head. There's no feeling except for yerselves in either of you," my father said sadly.

Whenever there was a row with Phoebe, I noticed he always spoke of the two of us as though we were as bad as each other. On this occasion, when they had both calmed down she said she had come back with her friend Ivy, whose mother was dying, and she was sleeping at their council house to give Ivy a hand to look after her. She said she had been about to get in touch with us but had so much to do that it had been impossible, and anyway she was here now wasn't she? My father had to believe this for his peace of mind as on many occasions in the past he'd had to believe her explanations when his common sense had told him they were lies.

Phoebe was now flashier than ever. Her face looked caked in make-up; her hair darker than it's natural colour; her fingernails were red and she wore a gold charm bracelet that hung from her wrist. She was wearing a shiny leather mackintosh pulled tight with a belt round her waist and high heeled shoes. Even though it was early morning, she looked as though she was dressed to go out at night. As she stood against the counter facing my father, she kept glancing at herself in the mirror in the centre of the chip fryer and primping up her hair. Then my Aunty Cissie came in and for a moment they both stared at each other. Cissie grunted a reluctant greeting and few minutes later Phoebe left the shop.

"My God Leonard, I don't know how yer put up with it," Cissie said.

"Put up with what?" my father answered angrily.

"If her was a daughter of mine, I'd alter her! Up and down at this time in a morning dressed like a whore."

Now look here Cissie, any more 'er that sort 'er talk and I walk out 'er this shop." My father was all of a tremble with emotion as he said this and, seeing how he was, Cissie made no further comment. Before she'd left, Phoebe had promised to call at our house on the one afternoon my father had off.

I was at work on that day so I didn't see her, but when I came in at night he was sitting staring at the gas fire with a face clouded with worry. It was apparent they'd had a row as I knew they would. He couldn't stop asking her questions as though she were a sixteen year old girl and she'd resented it as she was now a woman in her middle twenties. Furthermore, it had to be faced, that she was a hard, sexually experienced, pleasure seeking woman. Yet he was naive enough to still think that by giving her his advice on how to be a good girl, she'd take it. I had foolishly tried to explain how useless this was to him, but he always dismissed me angrily as not knowing enough about life myself.

"Look what a bloody mess you've made of it," he'd say, and as there was no answer to that, I kept my mouth shut. It was 'least said soonest mended' as far as I was concerned about our Phoebe.

I was now working for the Co-op in the stores. Sometimes I had to go out with the vans, and being about the town I could see how the world was changing. Although it was only a few years after the War, the time before the war seemed to be a world away. There were motor cars everywhere and the horses had all disappeared. There seemed to be more young people and they were different to what young people had been before. The men in caps who stood at street corners smoking fag ends were nowhere to be seen; the bus companies began to use double deckers and a few wealthy people had televisions with little smoky coloured screens. The first I saw working was in the electrical dept at the Co-op and I thought nothing of it at the time. I put it down as just another gadget. The post war world was filled with them.

The old dolly tubs and dolly pegs were replaced by washing machines. The heavy iron mangles that I had to maul with as a boy on washing day had gone along with the cart horses, and were replaced by smart rubber rollered wringers. The new gas stoves were white, elegant looking affairs and there were great developments in all kinds of household fittings. The old range grates that had been at the heart of working class families were whipped out and replaced by neat little tiled affairs. Hygiene was much more to the fore. There were no longer piles of horse muck in the streets; young women began to read new women's magazines filled with stories and images of cosmopolitan life. These unsettled them; made them want the gadgets in the shops; made them want to have a different life to what their mother's had had to put up with; the masculine world that existed before the war began to crumble.

Even in the chip shop, changes were afoot. Cissie had begun to sell fried chicken, which before the war had been a luxury, only tasted at Christmas, and was now so plentiful that people had it with chips instead of fish. She also began to fry sausages. Her menu was much extended, and in those post war years, the shop came to it's full pomp. It's reputation was known all over the city. The tripe she sold was said to be the best ever tasted by regular tripe eaters. The dining room was so much used, the seats round the table had to be replaced. It seemed at that time it would go on forever.

Cissie was a bit bonier, her face a bit fiercer, her back a bit more bent, but she was as strong as ever about the place. Her energy seemed inexhaustible. Twelve hours or more a day working at the back of the counter against the hot chip machine was nothing to her. My father was now an old man worn down with complaint and worry. But he'd always behaved like that and didn't seem any different to me. Certainly, he'd made the shop his life although he was only paid a meagre wage. Herbert Pepper came in occasionally. His son Norbert had brought shame on him. He'd been summonsed for cutting a massive swastika on the bowling green in the park, and Herbert was very subdued by this. It was some measure of how things had improved between my father and him, that my father never mentioned the swastika.

My Aunt Cissie was not so sensitive. She said when they were both there, "I'm glad I never had any kids. Mind you if I had, I'd a brought 'em up a lot different than you pair have. I could tell as soon I saw, what d'yer call him . . . Norbert, that he was no good."

She laughed to herself as she spoke the name, as though it was ridiculous and Herbert visibly winced. Then she turned on my father. "Her should be ashamed of herself, Phoebe should; but then there's no shame in her. All her's ever thought about is dolling herself up for men. By God what would me mother a' said; her'd a killed her."

"You've never had any kids, so you've no right ter talk!"

"I can express myself on any subject I want Leonard. This is a free country."

My father made no reply to this as he knew it was useless. They had many times argued before about it and as far as trying to defend Phoebe's conduct in any way, he'd long since given up.

During the few months after she'd come back, Phoebe did often call on us, and when she did her vitality filled the house. It reminded me of when she was a young girl. Everytime she came through the door, she'd put her arms round my father's neck and kiss him and promise all sorts of things.

I knew she was telling him lies, and he knew it too, but the fact that she wanted to make him feel good about her was enough. It had to be. After these visits, he'd often be more depressed than ever, as he was now forced to realise that his little girl would never live at home again, and it made me realise how much the world of the chip shop meant to him. His sister Cissie had not only dug herself a little gold mine and founded a local institution, she'd also provided her brother with a meaning to his life.

Like most people I often wonder about the chanciness of existence; how some things happening affect our lives and some don't. Why it is that some die young while others live into senility? What the process of selection is and if there's one at all. Is it really a tale told by an idiot full of sound and fury, signifying nothing or is there some pattern to even the most random happenings? Needless to say my wondering never gets very far in this matter, and I always end up by going out by the same door as I went in. But what I do observe is that the mind, in retrospect, often makes the most bizarre and strange happenings seem inevitable. Certainly the tragedy that was to occur in the Salt family and shock the whole town at the time now seems to me to have been fated. It was as though the great playwright that writes the script of reality each day; the genius that created Hitler and Mr. Churchill to play the parts they had to play; the force that named Napoleon, King Farouk, and Idi Amin; that even gave my Aunt the name of Cissie, excelled itself in the creation of this next act, which although it was certainly tragic also had it's comic side.

Chapter Eleven

Just after the war, the field that held the annual wakes in this town was designated by the Council for development. It was proposed to build old peoples bungalows on it and so the wakes had to find new lodgings. For a few years they used the waste ground at the back of the Colosseum directly opposite my Aunt Cissie's shop. Then there were complaints from the residents in the street and so it had to move again, this time to the very centre of the town, where half the wakes were on a car park behind the Town Hall, and the other half in front of the Town Hall. Very old people said they remembered it had been there in their younger days. Certainly it lit the town up and did great business, especially after the pubs closed at night. There were the usual catch-penny stalls filled with slot machines. There were coconut shies, rifle ranges, dobby horse roundabouts for children, dodgems for adults and there was what I can only call a chair-o-plane, which was like a big roundabout with many chairs attached to chains that, when it was going round, swung the occupants in a broad and stomach churning arc.

This wakes I write of was not the annual wakes. That was always held in the first week of August. This was one of a number of smaller travelling fairs that called on midland towns at that time. They rarely stopped for more than three days and mostly came in the winter months. This one came on a Thursday afternoon and in a few hours was set up and ready for business on Friday night.

I was on my usual drinking rounds that night, and as I stood in the bar of the Leopard I could see the coloured lights from the stalls reflected in the window, and there was a great bustle in the bar as the fair had attracted more people than usual to the town. The barmaids were very busy and I remember being pleased by all the activity. I felt that it would be a good night and so I had my usual quota of half pints in the Leopard, then walked across to the Duke and had a couple there. As I stood at the corner of the square trying to make my mind up which pub to call at next, I could see the whole of the centre of the town and the Town Hall lit with a thousand coloured bulbs. It was like I imagined Blackpool illuminations would be. I certainly had never seen the town look so splendid before. It had a magical look about it like some strange medieval fairyland. The whole square was alive with hundreds of people and the throb from the great traction engines was like a pulse beating.

For a while I was transfixed, then I decided to call at the

Star where they usually had the piano going on Friday night. Sometimes a man with a mouth organ would join in. It was a great dark barn of a pub with ceilings so high above the electric light bulbs that they were hardly visible. The varnish on the bar and the tables had been worn away by years of being wiped with a damp cloth and the great stove pot was always filled with coke, sometimes to such an extent you couldn't sit near it for the heat. There was also a smaller stove in the little snug next to the bar, where Mrs. Potts and various other old women sat and beyond this, down on the other side of the passage leading to the lavatories, there were two big dark smoke rooms. One was hardly ever open; the other was used by courting couples and men with other men's wives.

This pub was used by all the boozers from the poverty stricken end of the town and as I stood there at the bar, the place was full of them, and the man who played the piano was beginning to make a tinkling start. Then the door opened and a man known as Kowk, which was short for Colclough came in. He looked a bit flustered and I saw him tell the people at the table nearest to the piano something. I noticed they seemed shocked.

A second later when he came to the bar he said, "There's been a wench killed at the wakes. Flung out 'er that hurdy-gurdy thing. Her'd hit the front 'er the Marquis 'er Granby with such a bloody smack it turned me sick. Then I heard the bloke as picked her up say her's a gonner, her neck's broke."

The publican and the barmaid and the people round the bar all began to gabble at once.

"The hurdy-gurdy? There is no hurdy-gurdys now man," the publican said.

Kwok looked perplexed for a second and then he began to try to explain. "It's that thing as whizzes round fast and folks sit on chairs. One a the chairs broke off it's chain and sent her flying. Her hit the front'er the pub such a bash yer could hear it yards away."

To this I was listening with as much interest as anybody else round the bar, when he said something that brought me into full attention.

"Somebody said her came from down Stringer Street. I"ve seen her many a time. Her's a smart looking wench."

For some reason I can never to this day understand I knew it was my sister Phoebe he was talking about. I cannot remember exactly what I did next. I know that I left my drink on the counter, rushed out and ran toward the fair. When I got there although the music from the dodgems was still playing there was a strangely subdued feeling among the crowd. In front of the Marquis of Granby were two policeman, one an Inspector, who was looking up at the front of the pub. In the doorway there was a black man who looked drunk. I knew him by his nickname of Cherry Blossom Padawax. As he saw me he staggered across, his eyes hazy with drink and he began to say something. At first I couldn't understand him, then I made out that he'd seen what had happened and I knew he knew Phoebe was my sister.

"I tell you man," he gasped, "I saw her flying through the air; her was screaming or her might even a bin laughing like wenches do when they get excited, then . . . bash. Her felt nowt; her was dead as soon as her hit that wall. It must a thrown her thirty yards. Just one smack and her was gone."

On hearing this I pushed my way to the police Inspector, told him I thought it was my sister and asked where they'd taken her. When he told me which hospital I was in two minds whether to rush there or to go down to the chip shop to find out if my father knew what had happened. I decided to see my father and made my way through the crowd towards the Waterloo Road. As I hurried there I knew that this would break him. It would be more than he could stand. Of all the people in the world, he loved Phoebe most. Nothing she'd done or could ever do would diminish his feeling for her. I sometimes thought that all the pain he'd suffered because of her had only served to fuel his love.

When I got to the chip shop there was a queue of people waiting to be served and my Aunt Cissie was at her usual place behind the till and for a second I thought they hadn't heard. But when she saw me she beckoned into the back room and told me my father had heard and had rushed to the hospital in a taxi. I started to talk to her about it but she said she was too busy and went back behind the counter where two girls were serving.

I decided then that I'd go to the hospital was well, and rushed to the taxi rank. There was no taxi waiting so I stood, raging against all taxis and taxi drivers and the fate that had befallen our family that night. Why! Why! I fumed to myself. Then a taxi drew on to the rank and I got in and asked the driver to get to the hospital as fast as he could. As we sped down the main road I wondered why I was hurrying. She wasn't going die before I got there. She was dead and would be dead forever. I realised it was my father I was worrying about. I was frightened of what I'd see when I met him. Would they let him see her. She wouldn't be in a ward, she'd be in the mortuary. I was terrified of having to go into a mortuary. The zinc tables, the running water, the smell of death, the ghastly doors shut on the slats where the bodies lay on slabs. My mind was filled with these horrors as the taxi drew up at the accident unit.

A few minutes later I was walking down a polished corridor following a nurse. I remember thinking she'd got a big behind, then wondering at what a horrible mind I'd got. In the midst of tragedy it had a coarse streak running through it. The nurse opened a door and as I followed her I saw my father sitting on a bench against the far wall. He had a vacant look about him. I learned later that he'd been given a sedative. I went and sat down beside him and as he looked across at me I could see his face was a mask of frozen pain. His eyes seemed pulled in different directions and his bottom lip hung looser than I'd ever seen it before. He tried to say something but couldn't articulate his words and I attempted to put my arm round his shoulder but he shrugged me away. Then he spoke.

"Her's gone, I've just seen her lying there. Her was smiling like when her was young." Then a groan came from deep inside him. "Oh Phoebe, me little wench. Her's gone, gone, we shall never see her again."

I felt the tears well up in my own eyes. I had never seen another human being in such pain. Then I saw him make an attempt to pull himself together. He sat up straighter and wiped his eyes with his fingers. "Her's gone and there's nowt we can do about it."

Then for some reason even at such a terrible moment as that, when I was filled with deep emotion or at least it felt as though I was, a line from an old song came into my mind.

"She flies through the air with the greatest of ease,
The daring young woman on the flying trapeze."

There was nothing I could do to stop it and no sooner was it there than I felt nauseated. What sort of a human being was I? What did I feel? Was I just pretending to myself that I felt anything at all? My father knew nothing of this thank God, and a few minutes later, the nurse asked me to take him home as there was no point in staying any longer. He'd identified the body and that was that. Nothing would bring her back to life again. We slowly made our way down the polished corridor and out of the hospital where there was a number of taxis waiting and before long we were back at home.

My father had not spoken during the journey, but when we got in he said, "Her'd got tattoos."

"I knew her'd got one on her knee but I didn't know her'd got others." I tried to sound not particularly interested.

"Her'd got a bluebird tattooed on her shoulder as well, and

her'd got two letters tattooed on her breasts."

Letter, what letters? I said, mystified.

"I didn't want look. I could hardly read 'em but they were there clear enough," he said hopelessly.

"Letters," I said again. I was both sickened and mystified by this piece of information.

"One letter was M and I think the other was B, but I can't be sure. I can't be sure of anything. I don't want be sure." He groaned again, and I began to make him a cup of tea. For most of the night he just sat here looking at the gas fire.

When I tried to get him to go to bed, he said he'd rather stop downstairs so I left him and went to bed myself. As I lay there in the darkness I kept trying to think about what the letters might mean. Were they perhaps the initials of one or another of her men friends? Somehow I didn't think so. There was another thought in my head that I hardly dared think. Suppose in one of wild moods she'd had the letter M and B tattooed on her breast to represent mild and bitter beer. I knew she was mad enough for this and no sooner had the thought occurred than I knew it was the true explanation. I also knew that my father wouldn't understand as he never went into public houses. How terrible it would be if he found out.

The more I thought about Phoebe's tragic death, the more I realised that her end was perfect for her. It was as though fate had used it's imagination and fashioned a death to fit her personality perfectly. The letters on her breasts were part of it. She'd defied everybody, done just as she liked and never mind the consequences. She hadn't burnt the candle at both end; she'd chucked it in the fire. All I hoped was that my father never came to understand what the tattooed letter on her breasts stood for.

In the next few days, there was a numbness in our house. My father didn't go to the chip shop but I went to work as I was glad to get away from him. I had no idea what he did during the day. When I left him in the morning he usually sat staring at nothing and when I came back from work at night, he was still sitting there.

By this time the reality of what had happened had sunk into me and I seemed to feel nothing, but at the inquest I had to pull myself together as my father was on the point of collapse and was unable to answer the coroners questions. The verdict was accidental death. There was a police inquiry after, but both of us were in such a dull haze of pain that it meant little to us. Phoebe was dead and nothing would bring her back. Whenever I tried to have a conversation with my father, he looked at me as though he hardly knew me. He seemed completely cut off from reality. I had to make all the arrangements for the funeral. The undertakers name was Arnold Titley. He had buried my mother and was very helpful.

I had known Arnold when we were both boys at school. His family had been in the undertaking business for generations. He once told me his Grandma used to lay people out and take him with her. When she'd finished she used to lift him up to look at the corpse saying, isn't he or she beautiful, then horror of horrors, she'd tell Arnold to kiss the body. I can remember how I shuddered on hearing this, but on reflection I can see how it was good training for anybody in the funeral business.

He had grown from a fresh faced cheeky little lad, to a tall, balding fresh faced cheeky looking middle aged man who you would never guess had anything to do with death. When he came to our house, he at once began to reminisce about schooldays. This irritated my father and he asked him to get on with the business of the funeral. Arnold asked if my Aunt Cissie was coming and I unthinkingly said "Yes". But when I called in at the shop to tell her the day and the time of the funeral, she rounded on me.

"Whatever gave you the idea that I was coming? I'm opening the shop as usual. I went your mother's funeral, that was enough. I don't hold with all this funeral going. It's nothing but a money making racket. All them flowers rotting there. You tell yer father I'll be behind this counter as usual."

I tried to remonstrate with her by telling her how upset this would make him, but this made no impression on her. "Oh he'll get over it. Tell him get off his backside and get back 'er this counter again."

At this I shrugged and was about to leave the shop when she shouted.

"He'd no need come ter my funeral. None of yer had."

When I got home and told him what she'd said, his face tightened.

"I thought as much. Her's a hard woman Cissie is. The hardest I've ever known," he sighed.

"Her wants know when yer thinking 'er going back," I asked. He looked across at me before he answered.

"I'll never step inside that shop again. Her can rot in Hell as far as I'm concerned, Cissie can," and from that day on he never did.

For him it was a death-in-life. The shop was his life and he was too old and set in his ways to make another way of living. I

knew this when he said it and I think he knew it as well. I also
think he half expected Cissie to ask him to come back. He was
certainly the only person in the world she seemed to have any
affection for. But Cissie was stronger than he was and much
more stubborn.

On the day of the funeral, circumstances conspired to
illustrate the hopeless rift that the death of Phoebe had opened
between them.

When the cortege of the hearse and one solitary funeral car
arrived at our house, Arnold Titley told us that we would have to
go down the Waterloo Road to the cemetery as the usual road
was blocked with roadworks. He knew nothing of the rift between
Cissie and my father and didn't understand what anguish this
would cause as we would have to pass the chip shop. But there
was nothing we could do about it and I sat in the funeral car
sharing the tension I could see in my father as we approached
the shop. Then as luck would have it, the traffic lights at the
corner were against us, and we stopped directly outside the shop
where we could clearly see my Aunt Cissie working behind the
counter. When she looked up I am sure she saw us and those
moments I shall never forget. I made some comment about the
traffic but he didn't reply. He just stared out of the car window,
his face a mask of raw pain.

A few feet in front of him, his daughter was in her coffin
being driven to her grave, while a few feet through the car
window, his sister was frying chips. His life was being split in
two, and it could never again be like it was a few days before.
When we got to the churchyard it was drizzling with rain, and as
we stood at the open grave watching the coffin being lowered, I
remember thinking that the fir trees against the cemetery wall
looked like flue brushes. Then as I stared down into the hole I
thought of my mother's body rotting a few inches below. I
couldn't concentrate on what the parson was saying. All I knew
was that I wanted to get out of that churchyard, and even before
the little service was over I was edging my way back to the path.
My father stood still, staring down at the coffin as I began to
walk toward the gate. Then as I stood by the funeral car with
Arnold Titley and the driver of the hearse, we all had a smoke.

"We've got three more terday," Arnold said looking at his
wristwatch. "The next's at the crem at one o'clock. We are always
busy this time of year. It's the cold weather. It kills the old 'uns
off."

"There'll be a lot there," the driver of the hearse said. "He
was a Buff, a Worthy Primo. They all come, the Buffs do when

there's a funeral." He flipped his fag as he said this and a moment later my father came out of the churchyard.

He stood staring up the road and said, "Well there's one thing about it, I'll know where her is now."

I was amazed that he'd taken it so stoically. He seemed emptied of all emotion and was now prepared to get on with his life. But when we got home I soon found this wasn't so. He slumped back in his chair and did nothing but stare at the fire and for the next few weeks he hardly ate anything. I tried to get him out of the house as he'd always said he never been anywhere beyond the end of the street in all his life. I bought him a Travelmaster ticket from the local bus company. This entitled him to travel on any route throughout the county. He never used it. I asked him to come out with me for a drink at night but he refused. All he did was sit with the wireless on. I do not think he listened to it, but he had it on from morning to night. I was glad to get out, away from him.

I still called occasionally at the chip shop as the fact that my Aunt Cissie hadn't gone to the funeral didn't upset me. It was so much in character that I should have been surprised if she'd behaved any differently. Whenever I went in she always enquired after my father, and I could see she was missing him.

"Tell him not to be such a bloody fool. Tell him I want ter see him. His place is here, behind this counter."

When I got home and told him what she'd said, all he did was look at me as though I was a traitor for having gone into the shop.

Chapter Twelve

There were, at this time, certain developments in the Waterloo Road that directly affected my Aunt Cissie. A hundred yards beyond her shop was a Chinese Laundry run by a Chinaman named Ah Fat. He'd been there for years and on occasion I had my best shirts laundered by him as he got them up very nice. But times were changing and washing machines were more plentiful and better designed. Poor Ah Fat was feeling the pinch. He'd a number of black button-eyed young children to rear and had to find another way of earning a living. So he sold his shop to Horace Caddy, a local business man.

This Mr. Caddy was known as Brassy. The nickname suited him perfectly. He was a florid faced man whose skull was always sweating. He was about sixteen stone of soft flesh, but for all this bulk he fluttered. That is the only word I can think to describe his movements. He was hardly ever still. His eyes swivelled constantly, like a trapped animal looking for an escape. He never finished a sentence and talked so fast that a thin dribble of spit came from the side of his mouth. He put me in mind of how I imagined a Turkish eunuch would look. He had tried many businesses in his time. He'd owned a number of slot machines. He'd been in the taxi business, or at least he'd owned two broken down taxis. At one time it was reckoned he'd made a pile out of house clearances. His career was littered with fresh starts that never came to anything. But as the men in the bar said, he'd always managed to live without work, and that to them was accomplishment enough.

Anyway it was brought to my Aunt Cissie's notice that Brassy was going to open up a new chip shop in direct opposition to her. He'd no doubt seen and heard of her being the wealthiest woman in the town and come to the conclusion that he could do just as well if not better. So Ah Fat's laundry was boarded up for a few weeks and much humping and banging was heard.

There was a lot of talk in the place, especially in my Aunt Cissies' about this new chip shop. It even drew my father out of his melancholy. He said Brassy must have given somebody on the Council a backhander to get planning permission, as it had become necessary at that time. My Aunt Cissie was furious. How could such a thing be let happen. The Council wanted kicking out. She would go over their heads and see the M.P. Surely there was something against it. When I pointed out that Brassy was only doing what she'd done and was always advocating, using his enterprise to make his way in the world, she rounded on me angrily and told me to shut up.

But for all her rage and threats, the work on Brassy's chip shop went on and before long the builders' boards in front of it were pulled down and the new shop was revealed in all it's glory. Not that it's glory was much. It was evident that Brassy hadn't spent a lot on it. It was still the same little shop. There had certainly been no great beauty born. All that had been done to the outside was a bit of painting and pointing. There was a new sign over the door however, and this caused the most comment. It said in bright yellow letters, "Chish and Fips."

My Aunt Cissie was dumbfounded. Such thinking was completely beyond her comprehension. At first she thought it was a mistake by the painters. When I said it was a gimmick, she didn't understand what I meant as the word had at that time not come into general usage, and when I tried to explain my efforts it only seemed to enrage her. She even blamed me for it, as in her eyes I remained the younger generation, although I was in my forties.

"I don't know what the world's coming to these days. Everybody want summat for nothing. Nobody er'll have work. They make me sick. Yer want be at the back of this counter. Yer see folks at their worst and it isn't a very pretty sight I can tell yer."

Once she got started she went on like this and if I ever disagreed with any of her opinions or prejudices, she'd get very angry. It was no use pointing out the contradictions in her statements. She just wouldn't listen. The coming of the new chip shop provided her with a reason to berate the Council, the Government, human nature and particularly myself. She even contrived to blame my father, even though it was months since he'd stepped into the shop.

"He's never here when yer want him. I have ter do everything myself. Oh folks make me sick. They're all self, self, self," she complained.

When the new chip shop sold it's first chip, there came another bombshell. It wasn't Brassy behind the counter. It was Ah Fat and his wife with two of their eldest children and all the other children peeping from the back room. Obviously Brassy had only put money into it and Ah Fat was now the manager of the first Chinese chip shop in this district.

My Aunt Cissie thought this explained the sign over the shop window. She came to the conclusion that "Chish and Fips" was just the Chinese way of spelling fish and Chips and nothing I said could convince her otherwise. At first when the news was brought to her she just ridiculed the idea.

"The Chinese don't know how ter fry chips. The chips er'll all taste 'er starch," she laughed.

Then one of her customers handed her a little pamphlet on which there was a menu with all the items Ah Fat was hoping to sell. When my Aunt Cissie put her specs on and read it, she behaved as though it was in a foreign language. She began to mouth words, "Egg foo yung, bean sprouts, sweet and sour." Then she turned to me and handed me the paper.

"What d'yer make 'er that," she said in a hesitating voice.

"It's a Chinese menu; there's Chinese chip shops opening up all over the country," I answered.

"I've never heard anything so ridiculous in my life. What's the matter with English chip shops? Have folks gone mad? What does it say . . . Egg Foo Yung? What's that? I wouldn't eat muck like that if they were giving it away free."

"Well they're not giving it away free," I chipped in, "look at these prices."

She snatched the paper back and stared at it more carefully. "My God," she gasped, "One pound ten, one pound ten; oh folks er'll never pay that. It's a days wages round here. He's no idea. He won't last a month charging them prices."

But he did last a month and what's more he prospered. The Chinese food proved very popular.

"I don't understand how anybody can eat it," Cissie said whenever Chish and Fips was mentioned. She also picked up all the tales of empty tins of cat meat being found in Ah Fat's ash bins and as he hadn't got a cat, according to her, he was using the meat in the fancy food he sold. But for all her carrying on about these foreigners I noted that she began to sell Curry Sauce and use the white plastic containers that Ah Fat had introduced into the town. Yet despite these innovations, on the subject of chips she remained a confirmed reactionary.

"The simple straight forward English chip's what people want, not this fancy muck. God only knows what fat Ah Fat uses ter fry 'em in but his chips are terrible. There's no tater in 'em. They're all batter. They tell me if he's got any left at night, he fries 'em again next morning. I'd never do that. They go black if yer leave 'em overnight, but it doesn't seem to worry him. He just dips 'em in the fat again and sells 'em. I'm surprised nobody's been poisoned. One woman told me as her'd been on the lavatory all night after eating some. Still, I'm not surprised; folks round her are that daft, they'll eat anything."

The doings of Ah Fat provided her with a constant source of

tittle tattle. Usually she didn't encourage gossip of any kind with her customers, but if the Chinese shop came up in conversation she was all ears and would avidly join in and add her bit to the gossip. Then another item of information was found that poured petrol on her fire. She heard to her amazement that there was an Indian restaurant opening called the Taj Mahal in the main street of the town where a boot and shoe repairers had been. This set her off again in another burst of indignation.

"Has everybody gone mad. This is England or supposed ter be in't it? They come here and take the bread out of our mouths, these foreigners do. In my opinion it wants stopping. They all want sending back where they came from. I'm straight John Bull I am and proud of it."

She ranted on in this way to anybody who happened to be listening and she usually ended up praising herself.

"I know what the chip business is. I've worked a lifetime in it and I know what my customers want. It's the old fashioned English Fish and Chips. None of this foreign fancy stuff. Although I say it myself, I've never had a complaint in nearly thirty years." This was a lie, as she'd had plenty. A few days before, one woman had sworn blind that she'd come in for a fried fish, and when she'd got it home, she'd found it was fried cow's udder. But Cissie took no notice of awkward facts like this. If she said she'd never had a complaint, she believed it, and that was the end of it.

Soon after she'd first heard the news of the Indian restaurant she began to hear reports of it's marvellous fitments. It had velvet wall paper, golden chandeliers and a painting on one wall of a snake charmer. All this deeply troubled her. The dining room she'd been so proud of was, after many years of heavy usage, looking battle scarred. No matter how the tiles were polished, they never seemed to be clear of a film of fat. Some of the tip up seats round the table didn't work and many of the salt cellars were dented and worst of all, on one table the original vinegar bottle had been stolen and replaced by a pop bottle. Cissie often said she'd have to spend some money on the place, but kept putting it off. I don't think she had any more big decisions left in her. Why should she bother. She was still doing as much business as she'd ever done. The little gold mine was still mining gold. Certainly Chish and Fips hadn't taken any of her customers, but for all this her tone was different. She had always been given to occasional bouts of self pity but now it became a daily routine.

"Here I am on my own, an old woman, nobody ter help me. I

have ter do everything myself."

This was not true as she'd always three of four girls employed either full or part time, though none stopped long as she was so demanding and difficult to work for. Also it began to be noticeable that she was becoming very suspicious of them. She'd often question them about what a customer had ordered and how much they'd charged. Then she'd stand recounting the money in the till. One night all three girls walked out after she'd accused one of them of putting a half crown in her shoe. She demanded that the girl take her shoe off and at once there was a big screaming do, and the girl threw her shoe at her. Then the girl's father came down cursing and demanding an apology. Cissie said she'd call the Police. The man told her to get on with it and there was another big swearing row before he went. This upset Cissie but not enough to allay her suspicions of being robbed. The fact that she couldn't trust anybody she blamed on my father, and as he wasn't there, whenever I called in she took it out on me.

I have a hazy sense of time, but by my rough calculations, it must have been in the early nineteen sixties when the Indian restaurant first opened, and Sissymints had been established nearly thirty years. It was now an institution. The name was known to everybody, for the town was a closed little world where nothing seemed to change. Then, suddenly, it was all over.

The young became a different breed whose horizons were much broader than their parents'. The young men grew their hair long and wore tight jeans, as did the young women. Everything they said and did and wore was strongly influenced by America. Music was everywhere, a new sort of music, not the old stuff sung in smoke rooms by baritones and tenors but a constant extrusion of noise punctuated by words like Baby, Baby, Baby, repeated again and again. Sometimes the phrase 'the people' was sung, as though the singers were advocating a new social order. It was as though there was a great party going on somewhere and all the young people were trying to get to where it was happening. It certainly wasn't happening in my Aunt Cissie's chip shop. She was completely oblivious to it.

If all the customers that used her shop had turned into monkeys she would hardly have noticed as long as they paid. She did however make comment about not being able to tell men from women any longer. I used to think in her case that neither category applied, as she was by now looking more like a scaly legged old hen than a woman. I remember at this time I went to the pictures one night to see a Cowboy film, and in it there was a scene in an Indian village. I think the tribe was the Crow. It had been a bitter winter and food was scarce in the wigwams and there was a lot of wailing from the squaws. One old squaw put her head out of the wigwam as the hero of the film passed by and I was struck at once by her resemblance to my Aunt Cissie.

My father was also beginning to show his years. He had difficulty getting up from his chair and often complained of the stiffness in his joints. He spent most of his day at home, but occasionally, if the the weather was warm enough, he'd put his hat, coat and scarf on and saunter down to the allotments at the back of our street where he had made a friend called Tom Jinks, an old collier who often gave him big onions, and every now and then tomatoes. Mr. Jinks was a tall, thin, bony big handed man who wore a thick black strap round his waist, and chewed twist. He had recently been presented with a certificate by the Coal Board to commemorate his forty six years service down the pit and he had nailed it to his lavatory door to remind him of what a bloody fool he'd been. His sardonic pit humour suited my father who was very proud of having worked in the pit himself and used to say 'once a collier always a collier'.

Association with a man like Mr. Jinks helped him over his depression after the death of Phoebe. That they were all men down the allotments was such a change for him after working for years with Cissie bossing him about. It released an aspect of his personality that had been crushed at the shop. For the first time in his life he had a mate.

One day as he was coming out of the allotment gate, he was nearly run down by two youths on a two stroke motor bike, who against the law, were using the paths as a dirt track. As the bike swerved to avoid him, it slipped sideways into the privet hedge.

One of the leather clad youths got to his feet and shouted, "Get out of the road you stupid fucker. You should a been dead and buried years ago."

My father was stunned and frightened by the ferocity of this attack but Tom Jinks who heard it wasn't. In a flash the allotment gate opened up and out he stepped, taking his jacket off.

"Get yer bloody cloth off," he roared. "Come on both on yer. I've told yer about riding down here. Come on let's see how tough yer are, yer yeller bellied young twats."

As he said this he put his big fists up in a fighting stance. For a moment the two youths were startled by his ferocity. Then one of them began to argue. But Tom Jinks stepped toward him and stuck out his grizzled chin.

"Get out 'er my bloody sight or I'll splatter yer face across that wall like a patch'er cowshit."

He said this with a venom that neither of the youths could match and they began to retreat. To save face, one of them muttered something about not wanting to fight an old man. At this Tom Jinks looked him up and down as though deliberating what to say. Then he spat out "Fuck Off" and turned and walked back to his allotment gate, turned again and as the youths pushed their bike away, stood staring belligerently after them.

My father told me this when he got home. "I don't know what this country's coming to; God knows what it'll be like in fifty years time. I'm glad I shan't be here for see it. They've been educated till they are bloody daft. They don't know what work is. They are pack rats."

The bitterness against the young was a regular theme of his. He'd begun to have a lot of trouble with local youths banging on his front door and generally making a nuisance of themselves in the street.

"There wants another bloody war; that 'erd soon stop 'em," he often said.

It was not long after this incident that something happened which was in it's way as significant to the Salt family as my Grandfather bringing that old iron chip cutter home from the moors years ago.

Chapter Thirteen

It was well known in the district that my Aunt Cissie was a miser. There were tales told, some true, of the extent of her meanness, and people said she must be worth a fortune. None of this troubled her. She minded her own business and said they should do the same. The trouble was that many of them had no business to mind. One of the tales told about her was that she kept money in a milk churn covered in chip fat beside her bed.

One day on hearing this from Norbert Pepper, a friend of his, a man called Steve Bundy, questioned Norbert further, and the outcome of it was that they both decided they'd relieve my Aunt of some of her spare cash. One day when she was working at the shop, they broke into her house and burgled it. They failed to find a milk churn, but they did find a small suitcase filled with half crowns and made off with it. When they got it to Bundy's Council flat, they realised that the half crown was no longer legal tender. They were very bitter and frustrated about this, but Bundy, being a resourceful fellow, decided to ask at Lloyds Bank whether the coins could still be cashed through a bank. The cashier told him that they could. So he brought about a hundred pounds worth to the bank and cashed them. The cunning fellow then decided not to overload one bank with half crowns but to spread them about a bit and taking a bus to the next town began to change coins at the bank there.

Meanwhile, my Aunt Cissie didn't notice the suitcase had gone for a few days, but when she did the cries that came from her were pitiful to hear. Her face contorted with pain, her whole body shook and as she clenched and unclenched her fists she wailed then screamed out aloud at the thought of her money being gone. Nothing could console her. The wound to her life was too deep. To listen to her you would have thought the whole of her fortune had been stolen instead of just a hundred or so pounds worth of old coins. That they were no longer legal tender meant nothing to her. She'd taken them over the counter and that was that. All she could think and talk about was how much she'd lost, and when the thought of somebody else spending what was hers came into her mind she declined to such a state that a doctor had to be called to tranquillise her.

The Police said the burglars were probably local and when they questioned her about who knew of the money she had no compunction about mentioning my father and me. We were both questioned at some length. Then they arrested Norbert and the youth Steve Bundy as the banks must have reported their exchanging the coins.

Life now became very difficult for my Aunt as she had clearly become mentally unhinged. She went on and on about her loss to everybody who came near her and although she had put every penny she took in the bank, she kept locking the till in the shop and rushing home to see if she'd been burgled again. Twice a day at least she'd phone the police station to find out if they'd recovered the money. She did this so often that the sergeant lost his temper with her. She reported him to the Inspector who tried his best to explain things reasonably to her. But after a few attempts, he lost his temper as well.

Then she began to question the girls in the shop as she got the idea that one of them was the girl friend of this Steve Bundy. She began to make all sorts of strange connections. One day it was Brassy who'd been responsible, the next she became suspicious of me and practically accused me of being an accomplice. I took no notice of her but the three girls working on different nights at the shop, who'd put up with her suspicions, all said they were going to leave if she didn't alter. When they confronted her with this ultimatum, her reaction was to shout at them.

"Somebody's been pocketing money, I'm sure of it. I haven't got eyes in the back of me head. Here I am, a poor old woman, and folks are robbing me right and left."

At this one of the girls, named Gladys, began to get her coat on. "I'm not standing for this. Come on she's off her bloody rocker," she said to the other two. Then she turned on Cissie. "Just pay me what you owe me and I'm off."

Cissie was taken aback and quickly realised that the girl meant it, and that she wouldn't be able to open if all of them went. As this realisation seeped through, she tried to pacify them.

"I didn't mean you Gladys. Yer know I didn't, I've always trusted you."

At this the other two bridled. "Oh, yer meant us did yer?" one of them angrily shouted at her. "Just pay us what you owe us."

All three girls were now standing waiting for her to pay them. Cissie was cornered and helpless for the first time in all the years she'd been at the shop and in spite of the rage of defiance that swelled up inside her, she managed to contain it.

"All right, I'm sorry for what I said. I can't help it. It just comes over me when I think 'er them pair spending my money. I just can't stop meself. Yer won't have ter take any notice 'er me."

She cried after she'd said this, sat down and put her hands to her head as though it hurt.

The girls seeing her in this state began to calm down and somehow it all passed off and the shop opened for business as usual. Yet in the weeks that followed it became apparent that Cissie's mental balance had been so deeply disturbed by the burglary that she was on the edge of a nervous breakdown.

That she had drawn insurance money for the break in, didn't pacify her. She regarded the coins that had been stolen as hers, and no other money could replace them. She could hardly bear to talk about anything else. Her mind was blocked and this was having an effect on her general health. Her bronchial trouble had become so bad that she had heavy coughing spasms many times a day. One day the coughing turned to retching, and her poor racked body began heaving to such an extent that she couldn't stand and the girls became frightened. They had never seen her so bad before and Gladys, the most responsible of them, decided to ring for a Doctor. He immediately rang for an ambulance and Cissie was carried out of the shop on a stretcher; it was to be the last time she ever went behind the counter or sold a chip.

When they got her to the hospital, they thought the retching was the sign of a heart attack, but after tests she was moved into a psychiatric ward to be treated for a nervous breakdown. When I went to see her, a few days later, she was so drugged she didn't know who I was and was clearly incapable of making any decisions about anything. I discussed the matter with my father and we decided to shut the shop and put a notice in the window saying that it was closed owing to illness. Although I didn't realise it at the time, that was the last day Sissymints was to open in Waterloo Road.

My father refused to visit his sister in the hospital but encouraged me to do so.

"It's your big chance; get yer foot in; her's helpless. You could be running that shop for her. It's your place; there's nobody else. It's yours yer daft bugger, grab it."

He kept dinning this into me and when I did decide to ask her about it I didn't realise it was a psychiatric ward she was in until I saw bars up to the windows and people shuffling up and down in dressing gowns muttering to themselves.

Cissie was sitting in a chair in the corner of the ward staring through the window. As I approached she turned and looked at me her face blank with no sign of recognising me. When I spoke to her, asking how she was, she didn't answer and I just stood there not knowing what else to say. I asked her how she was again, and her eyes began to blink as she attempted to focus her gaze on me.

"How would you be if you were in here? It's your father as is responsible for this lot." She said this in a droning, helpless tone of voice. "None of yer helped me when I needed it. Yer all turned against me."

At this I attempted to argue with her. "Yer should a come to Phoebe's funeral. That upset him yer know."

"Phoebe!" she spat the word out. "She shamed our family, that girl did. Up and down with trash. Why should I go to her funeral. What had her ever done for me. What have any of yer ever done for me. Here I am a poor old woman, helpless."

She whined on in this fashion for a few minutes. Then I attempted to ask her about the shop.

"What are yer going do about the shop. Shall I look after it for you?"

No sooner were these words out of my mouth than her face filled with suspicion.

"You look after it," she repeated. "What's it got fer do with you or yer father. He's put you up to this hasn't he. I know his thieving little tricks, but you tell him from me he'll never touch a penny 'er mine; none of yer will. It's mine. What I've got's mine and nobody else's. Do you hear me?" she shouted.

She was by now getting so agitated that her features were twisted and as she raised her voice a male nurse came across.

"Try not to agitate her," he said. Then he lifted her wrist and felt her pulse. "She's a very sick woman. Are you her son?"

"Him, my son!" she spat angrily. "He's trying to rob me. Him and his father are. They are after me money. Always have been."

I could see my presence was agitating her so I left the ward, and as I made my way home I realised that it was no use trying to reason with her. When I told my father what had gone on, he cursed her and said she'd never have made it without his help. He wished he'd never set foot in the place.

The shop remained empty for the next few months, then one day, I saw two men boarding the windows up, and later in the day a 'For Sale' notice appeared over the front door. I was so surprised at this I hurried home and told my father. He got his hat and jacket on and went to see the notice for himself. When he came back, he said he'd ring the Estate Agents to find out the particulars. They told him the manager of Lloyds Bank was acting for Miss Salt who was ill. We were both nonplussed at this and next day rang the bank to see if we could get any more information about the matter. But although the Bank Manager knew my father was Cissie's brother, he refused to divulge any more particulars. He just advised us to see Cissie.

My father suggested I should go to the hospital again. I flatly refused and said as he was her nearest relative, it was his place to go. We argued for several days. He kept on about his share, though I knew he had no legal right to a penny and the way she'd screamed at me in the hospital convinced me she'd give him nothing. But he hadn't given up hope and kept telling me to ring and find out how she was. I told him to ring if he was really worried. But he hated telephones and always avoided using them.

After a few days I could stand the arguing no longer and rang the hospital. She was no longer there. She'd been moved to St. Edward's the district mental hospital. This came as a real shock to us both.

"Her must be worse than we thought," my father said. "They wouldna have shifted her there for just a day or two. They keep 'em in there once they've got 'em. Her brain's gone; they never get better from that. Once the brain's gone, it's gone," he said solemnly. Then his eyes lit up. "Ring 'em up fer see how her is."

So I rang the Asylum and was told that she was no longer there either, but have been moved to a place called "The Laurels", a private nursing home. My father groaned. "A private nursing home?They'll have every bloody penny them buggers will. Now they know her's got money, they'll keep her alive. They're bloodsuckers. I'll bet it's costing her two hundred quid a week. Yer can bet somebody had a backhander at the Asylum for sending her there."

Then he laughed sardonically. "All that work, all that effort, all them years, and this is what it's come to. Her's always been a funny bugger but I never thought her'd go crackers. Still, I should go see her; yer never know what folks er'll do as have gone funny. Her might change her mind altogether. One day they'll think one thing, the next another."

The probability of Cissie changing her mind and leaving everything to us became the main item of his conversation in the next few days. Then something occurred which shocked him out of it. One day he went down the gardens to see his friend Tom Jinks and found him dead in his garden shed. When I came home from work, he was still trembling with shock.

"I didn't think he was dead at first. He was just sitting there in front of the stove as large as life. Why there was some mint in his hand. He must a just cut it before he died. One minute yer there in full flesh, the next yer a gonner. It's the best road for go, I suppose," he said staring hopelessly with his eyes glazed.

I could see that the transience of life was filling his mind. He was now seventy one. Cissie was two years older and both of them looked it. He had lost all his top teeth and had a plate of false ones made. But he never wore them and his cheeks were sunken in. This had changed the look of his face; made it more skull like. His skin was dry and had become yellower. He reckoned this was the result of chip frying for a quarter of a century. I joked that he resembled Ah Fat. This did make him smile as he often joked that Ah Fat rendered himself down to make the fat to fry his chips in.

After the death of his friend Tom Jinks, he stopped going down the allotments and began to sit for hours on end staring at the gas fire. Perhaps in the afternoon he'd saunter to the end of the street to watch the traffic pass. The high point of his day was when the the evening paper came through the letterbox at tea time; yet for all his unhappiness he still kept on at me to go and see Cissie.

I was now working at a sheet metal works doing general labouring but the firm was in difficulty and often we were on three days a week. Then the factory inspectors came and examined the canteen and lavatory facilities, which were practically non existent. They wrote a damning report demanding immediate improvements be made. The firm was in no position to afford this and all who worked there were expecting the place to close down any day. I didn't tell my father any of this as I knew it would only start him nagging me to get in touch with my Aunty Cissie again. He couldn't get it out of his mind that I was the nearest relative of hers after himself.

By rights if there was anything left after them bloodsuckers at the nursing home end had their share, it should be mine if only for the work he'd put in at the shop. "Yer want ter get yer foot in there man, and keep in in. Take no notice of what her says. You can bet her dunna know what her is saying from one minute to the next; I tell yer they'll have every bloody penny. It kills mar pig when I think about it. I'm only thinking er you. I shan't be here much longer and neither will her."

This was the main theme of most conversations and I went as far as to send her a birthday card and a Christmas card from both of us. We did get a little Christmas card back, not from her but from "The Laurels". He was very excited about this and reckoned it showed that the ice was melting. When I pointed out that it wasn't signed, he became angry.

"Yer've always got ter look at the black side 'er things, you have. You've always been the same. It's a card in't it. How d'yer think they knew our address? Her must a told 'em."

I had to concede that this must be true and as it was approaching Christmas, I decided to ring the Laurels up to enquire how she was. Filled with trepidation I dialled the number and in a moment, a very posh voiced young woman answered. I said I was ringing about Miss Cissie Salt to see how she was.

"Are you a relative?"

When I said I was her nephew, she asked me to hold for a moment and I heard her high heels clicking away and other faint voices in the background. I was tense as I waited trying to imagine what Cissie's reaction would be. A few seconds later came a plummy, sophisticated voice.

"I'm afraid that Miss Salt is sleeping at the moment. I would advise you to phone in the morning. She is quite well physically, but I'm afraid any undue excitement quickly tires her." And that was that.

When I told my father what they'd said, he immediately decided they were lying.

"They've got their hands on her and they'll milk her for every penny her's got." He told me to ring again and when I seemed reluctant he flared up and there was another row which ended with me telling him if he wanted to find out how his sister was, he'd better ring himself. For days we were not on speaking terms. Then, I read in the local paper that a new Chinese takeaway Called Charlie Chan's was opening and realised it was where Sissymints used to be. The news was of such importance that it broke the silence between us. My father was stunned.

"How can her a done the business? Her's supposed ter be off her head. I can't imagine her doing business with a Chinaman or anybody else. How can somebody as is in an Asylum be responsible for their actions, never mind sign legal papers."

He kept on about this till I was fed up of hearing him. Then he changed tack and started saying that there were certain things in the shop that were as much his as Cissies and that he was going down there to claim them. I believed this to be true so one morning we made our way to the chip shop which was still boarded up at the front. We went round the back and at once saw the place was gutted. Whoever it was that bought it was certainly spending a lot of money. The back wall of the dining room was demolished as the building was being extended. The upstairs ceiling was supported by iron struts and the place was a hive of noise and activity with the scream of an electric drill cutting through metal, drowning the clatter and banging that was going on. When we stepped over a pile of rubbish to get in we could see that the shape of the shop had been completely changed. It was no longer Sissymints. My father stood abashed. Whatever bits and pieces he'd come to collect had been either buried under the rubble or chucked away. Then I noticed a big skip full of rubbish outside the gate. I went and had a look in and recognising bits and pieces from the old shop. I lifted up a badly dented salt cellar.

"D'yer recognise this?" I asked my father who had now joined me. He stared at it, then he looked down into the skip and bending over pulled up what looked like a bit of old iron.

"I recognise this," he said holding the old iron chip slicing machine that had been my Grandfathers. At the moment I realised that a holy chalice had come back to our family; a chalice that symbolised the Salt family's association with the chip. As my father held it up I sensed that he felt the significance of the moment as well. We carried it home and as he stood it on the back kitchen table he turned to me and said, "By God that's seen summat in it's time. Life, death, madness, fire, the lot and there it stands. I wish Cissie could see it." When he said this the expression on his face changed. He touched the old iron machine and said sadly, "It wouldn't mean anything ter her though; her's too far gone."

Chapter Fourteen

At this point I must call a halt to this history of my family's association with chips. Sissymints has gone, Charlie Chan's has taken it's place and strangely enough this rather pleases me for no other reason than I used to enjoy the Charlie Chan films. Such are the curious connections that life in this century sometimes makes.

My father lived for three more years and died in peculiar circumstances. One day I came home from work and as I went in the back kitchen I could smell gas. I rushed to the gas tap, turned it off, opened the back window and went into the kitchen where my father was sprawled out dead in his armchair in front of the gas fire. At first I thought he had commited suicide, but then I realised that this was very unlikely as there was a newspaper lying on the floor where it had evidently fallen from his hand and I just couldn't believe that anybody would sit reading a newspaper while they gassed themselves. I remembered he was so mean he would often turn the gas fire so low that the slightest draught blew the flame out. Putting these two facts together I came to the conclusion that his death was the result of an accident and this was the verdict of the coroner. On his death certificate it said that he died of heart failure with irritation to his heart and breathing caused by North Sea Gas as a contributing factor.

Whatever the causes, he knew his time was up and I remember a few weeks before he died how I saw him standing looking up at a big poster on the hoarding at the end of our street. My heart sank when I realised what was on it. Two great red letters, M and B were advertising Mitchell and Butlers mild and bitter beers. When he came home after seeing it he took out a photo of Phoebe which he always kept beside his bed and sat looking at it. My father was not a very demonstrative man; the world he had been reared in did not allow for men to show or speak of tender emotions in public; it would have been thought of as unmanly. But on that day for the first time in all my life I saw tears in his eyes as he held the picture.

When he was buried and I saw his coffin lowered into the grave and knew that his remains were only a few inches from our Phoebe, I felt a great sense of contentment and when the sexton told me that the grave was now full it didn't trouble me much as I realised it was the end of an era.

The town was a different place, the last of the picture palaces was closed, television shops had opened and the Council decided to have the grime of the last century removed like a dirty skin from the Town Hall and various chapels. Streets were demolished, the people were moved to Council estates on the perimeter of the city and where the houses had been there were car parks. Everything seemed different; even the sky and the clouds looked higher and brighter. The closed in sense of containment had disappeared; the world was glossier and on the face of it, more appealing. But when you touched it, it was colder; the sensuality was different; the smell of aniseed and coal dust had gone and the chip shops were now mostly owned by either Chinese or Pakistanis, who sold all manner of strange dishes. It was almost impossible to find a straightforward English chip shop that sold the simple classical English chip any more.

One night as I passed Charlie Chan's I looked through the window and saw one of the girl assistants help herself to a glass of orange juice from a container in which two artificial oranges were floating round and round. I noticed she didn't put any money in the till and this little action summed up for me the way society had changed. The old structures had collapsed. The young seemed never to have heard of them. They just took what they wanted and assumed they'd a right to it. Heaven to them was Las Vegas.

My Aunt Cissie was still alive and sat all day staring through the window. I was told this by a man whose wife worked as a cleaner at The Laurels. One night I met this woman who was having a drink with her husband in one of the pubs I used. She said that Cissie talked to herself a lot and often seemed to be arguing with somebody called Len. Once when this woman had spoken to her, Cissie had said she wished she was just starting out on her life again.

It was in this same pub that one night I was standing in the passage with a half pint when the door opened and a group of people came in. At first I didn't recognise them. Then I saw that one of them was Alma's sister with a man I presumed was her husband. She was of course a lot older and looked it. I didn't think she recognised me, but then two more women came in behind her. One of them was blonde and flashily dressed and seemed very excited. For a second she stood with the door open talking furiously to the woman with her. Then she turned her head and I got a full view of her face. It was Alma. She'd dyed her hair and face was plastered with make up. She was wearing a white coat dappled with black spots. Her fingers were covered in big artificial gold rings and her fingernails were painted a vivid red. She made everybody else look drab. She had put on a bit of weight but was still an attractive woman. For a moment I stared at her dry-mouthed, then she turned full face and saw me and her expression completely changed. Her mouth opened as though she had suddenly felt a pain that had stopped her in her tracks. All the excited laughing of a second ago had gone. She put her arm out as though to support herself, then pushing one of her companions aside, she rushed towards me and put her arm round my neck.

I can't remember clearly what happened or what was said in the next few minutes. It was one of the most emotional times in my life. No sooner had I felt her body against mine than the memories of how it was when we were courting came back to me. When we had both calmed down I went and sat against her in the smoke room and she told me how she lived in New Jersey and had two children who were now grown up. One was a student at New York State University. She said this as though it was a quite a normal thing to happen and I thought as she said it that if she'd stayed here they'd have got no further than the Council School.

I saw her most days after this meeting and she poured out all that had happened to her since she'd left and it soon became apparent to me that she was deeply unhappy.

"If it wasn't for the children, I'd be here like a shot. I feel that my life's been split in two; half of me always wants to be here. You think this place is a dump and you're right it is a dump; but Oh God I yearn to be back. Look at my sisters, they both live in Council Houses. They've got nothing and they'll never have anything, but I wish I lived near 'em. Sometimes I shut my eyes and I can see the Town Hall and our front door. Yer don't know who you are when yer young, do yer. When I got on that boat I thought I'd never want ter set eyes on the place again; but after a few years I began to dream about coming home."

As she said this there were tears in her eyes and when I tried to comfort her she whispered, "I often think about you too; I think about how it was when we first started courting down by the canal, you remember."

Unfortunately I remembered other things as well but I went along with her mood of nostalgia and truth to tell when she stood close to me I clearly understood that she was the woman who'd meant most to me in my life. The sexual chemistry was still there between us. The night before she was due to fly back from Manchester Airport she was very tearful. She kept hugging her sisters and then trying to pull herself together. She kept making them promise to write to her every week. Then she put her arms round me and squeezed herself tight to my body as though she never wanted to let go and I was myself moved. My eyes were damp and as I said Good Night to her she asked me to go to the airport next day to see her off. I made some excuse as I couldn't face that.

I walked back home that night glad of just one thing; she hadn't seen me in the ghastly uniform that I have to wear when I am doing my job selling cockles and mussels round the pubs. For days after she'd gone back I kept thinking about her. Whenever I got out of bed in a morning and looked through the window and saw the usual view of the backs of the next street which I'd seen for most of my life, I'd think of Alma getting up in America and wonder why it was that some people left the place they were born and reared in and people like me are stuck for ever.

It is quite beyond me to imagine any other life than I've lived. I often wish that I'd gone into the army and seen a bit of the world like many other men of my generation. But somehow what has happened to me seems as inevitable as the shape of my nose, or the colour of my eyes and yet — when I think about cockles and mussels, I rage against what I am doing for a living. I know I am capable of much more. When I was at school, out of a class of forty two I was always in the top ten and one of the lads out of my year, a boy from a poor family, is now the managing director of a big company, another is an Inspector of Police. Neither of them was any brainier than I, but somehow in our family, the great achiever was Aunty Cissie with her chip shop. It is as though she was the one who climbed out of the hole and all the rest of us should look up to her; that the height of our achievements should be to own a successful chip shop. It seems that only chips were the answer to the poverty of the streets I was reared in.

Looking back I can see that Sissymints was the one solid achievement of at least three generations of my family and even that was a lot more than most families could boast about. Indeed if I ever let it be known that I am the nephew of Cissie Salt it causes people to look with some respect at me, and as I stand most nights by the gentlemen's lavatory looking down the Waterloo Road and see the lights from Charlie Chan's and feel the weight of my basket of cockles and mussels, I realise how far I've fallen down the social ladder. My father, once when angry, said I wasn't fit to lace Cissie's shoes and at these times I feel that it's true; but when I think of her sitting staring at nothing, mumbling to herself in her room at The Laurels, her mind still poisoned by the thought that people are robbing her, I wonder what it all amounts to in the end and was it worth it?

At this time in my life I am attending classes in local history at the W.E.A. and one Saturday we went to the local Museum and Art Gallery which had just been extended. I was fascinated to see a street of Victorian shops complete in every detail. There was a Chemist's, a Sweet Shop, a Doctor's Surgery, a kitchen from a working class house, a Parlour and a Chip Shop. They had cinema posters from a time when I used to go to the pictures two or three times a week. One of them advertised Edward G. Robinson in the Sea Wolf, a film I remembered well. Errol Flynn was on in the second part of the week in Captain Blood.

Seeing this chip shop moved me greatly as it closely resembled my Aunt Cissie's before she had it modernised. I thought of the old chip cutting machine I had at home and realising that it would fit perfectly into this reproduction, I contacted the Curator who made a fuss of me and was delighted to accept the machine. Now, when I visit the Museum, as I often do, I go and look at it and come away flooded with memories of my own and my family's life. And often at night, when I shut my eyes, the ghosts from my past life parade before me. And of them all, the one that brings me a stab of pain is my twin sister, Phoebe. For, unlike the others, she is always laughing as though she is having such a good time.

SHORT GLOSSARY OF
COLLOQUIAL WORDS

Page 3   *SCRUBBING:* Interesting work repeated often enough becomes as boring as scrubbing.

Page 3   *MAUL or MAULING:* Difficulty in moving heavy objects or even oneself.

Page 9   *CHOMMELLING:* Excessive and noisy chewing of food.

Page 15   *SCORP or SCORPING:* Angry complaint.

Page 16   *LOBBY:* A cheap and sustaining stew made from vegetables and scragg ends of meat.

Page 41   *SCRAWMING:* Miserly attitude towards money.

Page 49   *BLARTING:* Crying miserably.

Page 50   *WOOSTERCASTER:* Wild and flighty young woman.

Page 51   *POT BANK:* A works where pottery is made.

Page 67   *REAPING UP:* Remembering, usually unhappy memories.

Page 72   *SNAPPING TIME:* Workmen's breaks.

Page 82   *MONSTINK:* An over-proud man given to showing off.

Page 98   *HODGE:* Offal food similar to Chicklings.

Page 121   *BUFF:* A member of the Antideluvian Order of Buffaloes.

Page 121   *PRIMO:* An officer of that Order.

✳ ✳ ✳